Space &
Dark Skies

An astronomical miscellany
from the Isle of Man

Howard L.G.Parkin BSc. BEd. FRAS

This book is dedicated to my grandchildren

Eban, Summer, Nora and Rio

*"Freill dty hooillyn er y speyr,
agh dty chassyn er y thalloo"*

*("Reach for the stars,
but keep your feet on the ground")*

Front cover image: Langness *(Sue Jones)*

Back cover image: Milky Way over Langness *(Ron Strathdee)*

Title page: The night sky from inside the Herring Tower at Langness. *(Ron Strathdee)*

Copyright © 2021 Howard L. G. Parkin. All rights reserved. ISBN 978-1-83808-456-1.
The right of Howard L. G. Parkin to be identified as the author of this work has been asserted in accordance with the Copyright Act 1991.
Photographs and other images reproduced herein are © the author or from the author's collection except where credited otherwise.
No part of this publication may be reproduced, stored in a retrieval system or transmitted in any form or by any means, electronic, mechanical, photocopying, recording or otherwise, without prior permission in writing from the author.
Published by the author. Produced and distributed by Lily Publications (IOM) Ltd.

Introduction

Inspired by the space race in the 1960s, Howard Parkin has been an enthusiastic astronomer since a child and has become an accomplished and entertaining speaker on the subject throughout the world. Howard has been teaching Astronomy to adult education classes since 1985. He is a founder member, former Chairman (from 2004 to 2014) and is currently the Vice-Chairman and Press Officer of the IOM Astronomical Society. He is a member of the British Astronomical Association, the Society for Popular astronomy, the Society of Satellite Professionals International and the Astro Space Stamp Society. In July 2013, in recognition of his work in education and outreach, Howard was elected as a fellow of the Royal Astronomical Society, and in 2019 was awarded an honorary BEd degree by Chester University.

In 2013, Howard established an astronomy consultancy and promotions company AstroManx, and through his work, he obtained Dark Skies discovery status for the Isle of Man, initially for seven sites in 2011, and subsequently nineteen further sites in 2014. Formally leading to the Island being recognised as one of the best places to stargaze in the British Isles.

For many years Howard has been giving talks and lectures on the subject in the Isle of Man, throughout the UK and abroad, and on many cruise ships throughout the world. Howard also undertakes a monthly astronomy programme on Manx Radio and has appeared on television on a number of occasions talking about astronomy and the Isle of Man's unique dark skies.

With nearly 90 per cent of the world's population living in the northern hemisphere, this book, whilst based on the author's residency of the Isle of Man, can be used as a guide to the features in the night sky for stargazers nearly everywhere.

Throughout the book, there are some astronomical terms translated into the Manx Gaelic language. These are shown in *italics* after the relevant word in parentheses. A glossary of all of these words is included at the back of the book.

Contents

Foreword

Former NASA astronaut Nicole P Stott.

Look up!

When I think of my friend Howard Parkin, these are two words that definitely come to mind.

These are also two words that are permanently in mind after having the opportunity to spend some time on the International Space Station (ISS), where one of the greatest joys there every day was the opportunity to "look down". There is a humbling beauty and power that comes from considering different perspectives of who and where we all are together in this universe. While floating on a space station, there is no better way to do that than looking "down" towards our Earthly home, and here with our feet planted firmly on it, there's no better way than looking "up"!

Experiencing the stunning beauty of our home planet from that whole new perspective – the chance to float in front of a window and see Earth – there is, of course, a natural desire to see the places we're familiar with – the places where our family and friends are. The Isle of Man is one of those places, and Howard is one of those people for me.

I'm honoured that Howard asked me to write the foreword for his book.

A running joke in the circle of Howard's friends can be summed up as "It's cloudy, so here's Howard". I chuckle about this because it reminds me of looking down from the space station in search of the Isle of Man. I would float to the window with my camera whenever our orbit lined up to "maybe" catch a glimpse of it. I say "maybe" because it seemed like there would never be a clear pass of the Isle of Man. Out of frustration, a couple of months into my mission, I emailed a picture to Howard titled "IOM Day Pass" – it was all white. (Well, I thought it was funny). Later in the flight, though, during a night pass, I'm thankful that I was finally able to capture a clear image of the Island, like a jewel, sparkling with its unmistakable outline in the middle of the Irish Sea.

This image would have been captured during one of the "dark sky" nights that the Isle of Man is so well-known and highly and globally respected for. I'm thankful to Howard and the members of the Isle of Man Astronomical Society and to the people of the Isle of Man for understanding the beauty that comes through the appreciation and preservation of the "can't see your hand in front of your face" darkness experienced on the Island. It's a wonderful example of how some of the best ways to experience such incredible awe and wonder comes simply through respecting the nature of the place we live.

Howard is a storyteller. It's what allows him to bring a night sky to life even when it's covered with clouds. His stories, though, are not high tales but tales of the discovery of the universe that surrounds us all and the history of his Island home. Howard makes connections between the science of the observation of our night sky to the reasons why we send humans to explore this space that surrounds us, between astronauts in space and students on the Isle of Man, and to the importance of the relationships we have with the people we share our planet with.

I'm blessed to have flown in space and experienced our home planet from that special vantage point, but I'm even more fortunate to know people like Howard who can share the significance of who and where we all are in this universe together by helping us all to look up. Through this book, Howard shows us all how a passion for something really can lead to a life of meaningful experience. He takes us on a wonderful journey through the dark skies —- leading us back to Earth with a much better appreciation for our place here on this planet.

Nicole Stott
Astronaut, Artist, Author *Back to Earth*,
Founder *Space for Art Foundation*

Nicole Stott and the author on the Cruise ship "Viking Orion" – June 2018.

Chapter 1

From the International Space Station to the Isle of Man

On 16th October 2009, I was sitting, somewhat apprehensively, in the Manx Museum Lecture theatre, wondering, "*just how did this come about, and is this going to work?*" I was about to talk to a NASA astronaut *(Troailtagh spoar)*, Nicole Stott, onboard the International Space Station (ISS), which was orbiting the Earth *(Y Cruinney)* every 90 minutes. Thus, I would for a short time become the "Capcom" (Capsule Communicator) to an astronaut up in space for a short while, a role I recall from my youth when the first US astronaut Alan Shepard and later his other astronaut colleagues reported back to the Capcom at mission control, *"Everything is A.OK"*.

It all came about thanks to Chris Stott, a Manxman resident in the US. Chris's wife Nicole was a NASA astronaut. Thanks to NASA and the Stott family's generosity, Nicole and Chris gave up one of their family video links to talk to us in the Isle of Man during Nicole's first flight to the ISS. Chris is the founder and executive chairman of ManSat, a Manx registered Company, and has been the Isle of Man's Ambassador for Space since 2003.

The event was a unique "Live Link" from the ISS to the Isle of Man. Nicole, who was living and working onboard for three months, spoke with several Manx school children and I for over 50 minutes.

This event's origin can be attributed to a phone call I received in 2001 when Chris rang and asked if it would be possible for him to visit the new Isle of Man Astronomical Society (IOMAS) Observatory at Foxdale. We duly met up at the Observatory, and I was pleased to show Chris the premises and generally talk about astronomy and spaceflight. During the visit, Chris advised me that his wife Nicole was a NASA astronaut, appointed in 2000. Following the visit, Chris kindly sent me a photograph of Nicole, and a friendship ensued that was to lead to this live link some eight years later.

Throughout the 2000's I received numerous updates from Chris about Nicole's progress, including the possibility of Nicole being launched from Russia to the ISS in a Russian Soyuz spacecraft. In 2008, I learnt from Chris that Nicole had been assigned to her first mission and would launch to the ISS in 2009 for a three-month stay on-board the Space Shuttle Discovery.

In Spring 2009, I received a telephone call from Chris asking if I would consider hosting a "live link" to the Isle of Man with Nicole whilst she was "on station". She would speak with me and answer some Manx schoolchildren's questions about life on board this international outpost 400 kilometres (250 miles) above the Earth. I was incredulous at the idea but readily agreed, and the whole concept gathered momentum.

When an astronaut is in orbit, the astronaut's family is allocated several opportunities to speak via telephone and video connections. Chris and Nicole kindly agreed to give up one of these to enable the Isle of Man link up to take place. However, we were not allowed to talk or publicise the link until Nicole had successfully returned from her three-month mission on-board the ISS.

Having agreed to the concept through Chris's Company, ManSat, the necessary permissions from NASA, Manx Telecom and MNH were obtained, and the project gathered momentum. As can be imagined, such a video link is not as straightforward as a phone call. Various specialist equipment was to be installed at the Manx Museum. Manx Telecom supported the technical aspects and generously provided the necessary equipment and expertise to ensure everything worked smoothly. In the meantime, a competition was launched for the Island's secondary schools. Pupils were asked to submit questions they would like to ask Nicole, who had been launched to the ISS on 29th August 2009. Manx Telecom delivered and installed the various equipment. With the MNH Technicians' assistance, the equipment was tested with a live link to Mission Control in Houston a week prior to the event.

We received over 200 entries from the Island's six secondary schools, and we agreed that we would select a first, second and third from each of the schools. These three and 22 of their classmates would be invited to the Manx Museum for the event. At this point, it was intended that just the six winners would ask their questions live to Nicole.

Given the technical aspects of the link, we realised that we could not just have a question-and-answer session. If we had a technical failure, it would have been a non-event. So, I was asked to deliver an introductory lecture about Nicole and her mission. This would then hopefully be followed by the question-and-answer session. Furthermore, as NASA is a US Government taxpayer-funded institution, we had to advise guests that the video link, deemed to be an educational outreach event, would only comprise myself and the children asking the questions. The Manx Museum Lecture Theatre audience would have to remain silent. All the monitors on the ISS and at the Manx Museum would only show the various questioners and me. With 150 schoolchildren and 50 guests in attendance, the event took place at noon on Friday 16th October 2009.

My "warm-up" lecture went well enough, and following this, I moved to a table we had set up on the stage. We then awaited contact for the link with Nicole on the ISS. At precisely 12.30 PM, I was advised that we were "live", and my first words broadcast from the Isle of Man to the ISS were, *"Hello, is that you Nicole, hello Nicole can you hear us?"*

Getting no response, I then went on to say, *"We heard something"* then, to my (and the audiences) great relief, we heard Nicole's response, *"Got you loud and clear, I just answered the call, and the video should come in soon".*

The video image appeared, and I said, *"Here we go, we see you Nicole live and on-screen with the Manx flag in the background; that's absolutely fantastic".* Nicole responded, *"I see you guys as well, and you look very nice too".*

There then followed the six children's questions and the answers from Nicole. I quickly realised that we had gone through the six questions relatively quickly, so I asked one of my colleagues to get the students whose questions came second in the competition to come up as well. I vividly recall one of the students look of abject horror when they realised they were going to ask their question "live" to a real astronaut in space

Nicole answered each question in turn from the ISS orbiting 400 kilometres (250 miles) above the Earth and travelling at over 27,724 kmph (17,226 mph). Nicole was a fantastic host, with detailed answers to every question. These varied from *"What does the Earth look like from space?"* *"What's it like doing a spacewalk?"* *"How do you sleep in space?"* and *"how do you clean your teeth in space?"* Nicole gave us a tour of the Station. She showed us the ISS toilet, how to clean your teeth, how to get into a sleeping bag in zero gravity (by somersaulting into her sleeping bag), and how to sleep comfortably even whilst upside down.

The link lasted 53 minutes, during which time Nicole and her colleagues had travelled some 22,000 kilometres (13,670 miles) from off the coast of California to over the Indian Ocean. This is more than halfway around the planet. We had been advised initially that the live link was to last 20 minutes, but after about 30 minutes, I realised that we were still going. I recall thinking, *"well, I am not going to hang up".* I was later told that we did receive a text message on the screen at about 25 minutes, *"2-minute warning we have another conference",* but I did not see it (honest). Then at about 50 minutes, a message appeared, which I did see, advising, *"we need to end it soon, right now, please".* So, reluctantly we concluded what had been a most remarkable and memorable experience. A few hours later, I

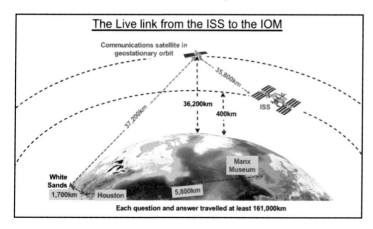

The Live link from the ISS to the IOM.

Nicole on the ISS and the author (lower right) in the Manx Museum. *(MNH)*

was delighted to be advised that Nicole had actually "tweeted" from the ISS about the event. Nicole had thanked me personally from space for setting it all up. At this time, I had never been tweeted before, never mind from orbit!

There were repercussions, however. Sometime later, in early 2010, Chris was on the Island and suggested that we meet up for a drink and a chat in the Terminus Tavern along the promenade near Onchan. When we met, with a stern expression on his face, he told me I was in trouble with Jean-Jacques Dordain, the European Space Agency's (ESA) Executive Director. He had been sitting in the ESA Control Room in Darmstadt in Germany, waiting to speak with the Commander of the ISS, ESA astronaut Frank DeWinne. They waited patiently for Nicole and me to end our chat so they could have theirs, but we just kept going. I was mortified, but then Chris grinned and said, *"They loved it; they thought the children's questions were wonderful"*. However, since then, I

Nicole's "Tweet" from the ISS.

20. GMT289/1230 Just finished videoconference w/Isle of Man schools. Thanks to Howard P for setting it all up. Was lots of fun! #onorbit3:09 PM Oct 16th from web

understand that similar calls are more strictly controlled. Chris then kindly presented me with a montage signed by Nicole showing images from her flight and the two mission patches.

A few months later, I received a call from Telefonica, Manx Telecom's parent. They asked if there was any possibility of Nicole and I linking up again, this time at the Company's annual conference in Miami. Of course, I responded I would be delighted to do so. They told me they would get back to me if they could arrange it with Nicole. However, a few days later, they advised me that as Nicole was currently training for her next mission on the Space Shuttle, she was unavailable. So, they did not want me after all!

What made this whole event special for me was the technology and the opportunity to participate in something unthinkable back in 1961, when Yuri Gagarin became the first man in space. It was also that

Montage presented after Nicole's mission. *(NASA)*

Nicole in the ISS with some Manx connections. *(NASA)*

everyone was impressed with the Questions, and I will never forget the children's faces before and as they asked theirs. Ian Longshaw, the School improvement adviser for the Manx Curriculum, said, *"Talking live to the International Space Station from the Manx Museum in the Isle of Man has got to be the ultimate in the "wow" factor. I'm sure it inspired everyone who saw her that they can realise their dreams through hard work and ambition".*

Immediately following the event, Chris Hall, the then Managing Director of Manx Telecom, said, *"This must be the longest 'long distance' communication ever made from the Island – from Douglas to a Space Station orbiting the Earth. It's not that long ago that a transatlantic phone call was a significant achievement, but the link up to the Space Station shows just how much the future for the next generation of Manx children is inextricably bound up with technology, and we were very happy to help make it all happen. Doing so involved a lot of hard work, and it was gratifying that NASA made a point of saying how much they enjoyed working with the Manx Telecom Team. We often get compliments – but getting one from NASA is certainly a first for us".*

There was to be an unexpected sequel. In February 2021, I was invited to talk to some children at Braddan School about space. Following my talk, their teacher told us about her experience as a Douglas High School pupil visiting the Manx Museum to see and hear an astronaut in orbit talking to someone from the Isle of Man.

Following Nicole's mission, the IOMAS was delighted to receive a Certificate of Authenticity from NASA confirming that items had been flown in space for the Isle of Man Astronomical Society. The three items in the photograph were also returned to us, suitably endorsed with an ISS official stamp on them.

This has always will be one of the most memorable events I have ever undertaken in my astronomical activities. It was a great privilege to have been able to do it. Thank you, Chris and Nicole.

ISS certificate of Authenticity. *(NASA)*

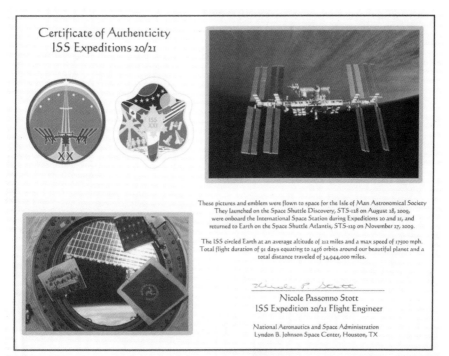

STS-133 Certificate of Authenticity

This flag was flown to space for the Manx National Heritage on the final mission of the Space Shuttle *Discovery*, STS-133. From her first launch August 30, 1984 until her final landing on March 9, 2011, *Discovery* has proudly flown over 148 million miles in 39 missions and logged a total of 365 days on orbit; the longest of any spaceship in history.

STS-133 total mission duration of 12 days, 19 hours, 3 minutes, 53 seconds, with 202 orbits around our beautiful planet and a total distance traveled of 5,304,140 miles.

Nicole P. Stott, STS-133 Mission Specialist

39th and Final Flight of the Space Shuttle *Discovery*
February 24, 2011 – March 9, 2011

National Aeronautics and Space Administration – Lyndon B. Johnson Space Center – Houston, Texas

Certificate presented to MNH by Nicole Stott, July 2012.

Chapter 2

The Heritage of the Manx heavens

In the Isle of Man, we have very clear skies, and there is evidence that the Island's night skies have been appreciated for millennia. The earliest record of any form of astronomical activity on the Island occurred in about 2000 BC. At Cashtal yn Ard in the north of the Island, a Neolithic monument was built and aligned to the rising and setting Sun (*Grian*) at the spring and autumnal equinoxes. This provides clear evidence that man built astronomically based monuments to commemorate their forefathers. This appreciation of the life-giving Sun has been of historical significance since humankind has walked on the planet.

Many believe that the Three Legs of Mann are a Sun symbol, denoting the Sun's passage from east to west. Whilst it is uncertain just when and why the Manx adopted the three legs as a symbol of nationhood, it is clear that Sun worship was important to the ancient Manx.

Interestingly, the three legs symbol is also used in Sicily. However, the fundamental difference between the Manx and Sicilian legs is that Sicily's ones are naked, whilst the Manx legs are clothed. Perhaps this is indicative of the Isle of Man's differing weather conditions in the Irish sea compared to Sicily in the Mediterranean.

In 1997, I became the Public Services Manager at MNH. A short time

The three legs of Man, the "Triskelion" – A Sun *(Grian)* symbol on Laxey Wheel.

later, I was introduced to John "Dog" Callister. He said to me in a broad Manx accent, *"Aren't you that astronomy fella?"* Upon giving a positive response, he asked, *"What's Raad Mooar Ree Gorree then?"* When I replied that I had no idea, he just said, *"Huh! call yourself an astronomer!"*

It is recorded that when King Orry arrived on the Island near the Lhen in the north of the Island in 1079 AD, he was asked where he had come from. He pointed up to the Milky Way and stated: *"Yonder is from whence I came, for along that way leads the road to my Kingdom"* I understand it was John Dog's great, great, great …. grandfather who asked him! Thank you, John, for adding this great snippet of Manx history to my astronomical knowledge.

The Milky Way is known in Manx Gaelic as "Raad Mooar re Gorree," or the Great Way of King Orry. A plaque commemorating the visit of King Harold of Norway in 2002, when he opened the Sound visitor centre, portrays this ancient Manx connection to the Milky Way. It shows the three constellations of the summer triangle, Cygnus: The Swan, Lyra: The Lyre and Aquila: The Eagle. All of which can be used for celestial navigation. Around the rim of the plaque is an inscription in the runic alphabet stating, *"Hail, Welcome here, you have come to the hall"*.

Between the 11th and 13th centuries, the Cistercian Monks at Rushen Abbey wrote "The Chronicle of Mann and the Isles". This is regarded as one of the oldest books known to have been written in the Isle of Man. It covers

Plaque at the Sound
Visitor Centre.

various aspects of life on the Island at that time. Included in the book are several astronomical phenomena.

An eclipse of the Sun took place on 1st May 1185 when the Sun was 92% eclipsed, as seen from the Island. This eclipse would likely have darkened the skies sufficiently for the brighter stars to appear. The Chronicles' actual quote states: "*In the year 1185 the Sun suffered an eclipse on the day of the apostles Philip and James such that the stars appeared*".

In 1639, Jeremiah Horrocks from Hoole, near Ormskirk in Lancashire, was the first astronomer to successfully predict a transit of the planet Venus across the Sun's face. Horrocks had calculated that such a transit would occur, however, he was unable to observe at the predicted time as he was a lay preacher and had to attend a matter of a "higher calling". Horrocks corresponded with fellow astronomer William Crabtree in Manchester regarding the date and time of the transit. Consequently, Crabtree is recorded as the first person to see a transit.

In 1901 the pre-Raphaelite artist Ford Maddox Brown was commissioned to paint a mural on the new Manchester Town Hall walls to commemorate this event. Brown needed a model, and he used the prolific Manx author Hall Caine as his model. The likeness of Caine to that of Crabtree on the mural is quite pronounced.

In 2002, I attended a Museums marketing conference for MNH in Manchester, and I was able to see the mural for myself.

Extract from The Chronicles of Mann and the Isles

The author in front of the mural of Crabtree observing the Transit of Venus in Manchester Town Hall.

In 1664 the Bishop of the Isle of Man, Isaac Barrow, became Governor of the Island. Bishop Barrow had a great interest in education. He founded the Bishop Barrow Trust in 1668, which ultimately led to the establishment of King William's College in 1833. Bishop Barrow had a nephew, also named Isaac. This nephew was the Lucasian professor of mathematics at Cambridge University, a post also held by the late Stephen Hawking. Isaac Barrow (the nephew) realised that coming up through the ranks of his undergraduates was an individual of incredible ability. Consequently, Barrow resigned his professorship at Cambridge, favouring his "more distinguished pupil". This distinguished student was none other than Isaac Newton, a man often referred to as the father of science.

A few years later, Bishop Wilson (Bishop from 1697 to 1755) was imprisoned at Castle Rushen, as he dared to disagree with the Lord of Mann. However, Bishop Wilson must have had some interest in astronomy as the following was recorded in his diary:

"The Annular eclipse of the Sun, 18th February 1736, began at 1-minute past 2 and ended 45 minutes past four in the afternoon at Bishops Courts – by the dial not by the clock".

When we consider the distance to the stars in astronomy, we use the light-year (ly) as a unit of length. Light in a vacuum travels at a speed of 300,000 km (186,000 miles) in one second. So, the distance light travels in one year is 9,500,000,000,000, nearly 10 trillion km. Considering the heritage links to astronomy on the Isle of Man, it is interesting to note that the light we observe from the star Rigel in the constellation of Orion left that star over eight hundred and sixty years ago when Peel Castle was under construction. Similarly, the light from the star Betelgeuse, also in Orion, left that star about six hundred and forty years ago, when Rushen Abbey was still a working monastery prior to its dissolution by Henry VIII in 1548. In late 2019 and early 2020, it was noticed that Betelgeuse was dimming far more than was expected. As a consequence, the distance is under review and Betelgeuse is now thought to be further away.

Following the invention of the reflecting telescope by Isaac Newton in 1761, George Quayle (1751-1835), a prolific businessman from Castletown, used the design of such a telescope to build a similar instrument. However, he likely made it with an interest other than astronomy in mind. The telescope does not elevate more than about 10° to 20° above the horizon. This indicates that perhaps the telescope was built for more nefarious means, possibly to assist with looking out for the UK revenue men. At this time, goods were legitimately imported to the Isle of Man in what was known as the "running trade". This was regarded as smuggling by the adjacent Isles' authorities.

The Constellation of Orion over the IOMAS Observatory. (*Dave Storey*)

The Quayle Telescope in the Nautical Museum, Castletown, IOM.

There are numerous records in the Manx Museum library regarding many astronomical events seen over the years. These include a meteor seen in Manx skies in December 1867 and the obituary in 1908 of *"probably the foremost astronomer in the Christian Ministry ranks"*. The Reverend Robert Killip had frequently lectured on astronomy. He had his own Observatory and had travelled to Spain in August 1905 to see a total eclipse of the Sun. The Manx Museum records also contain details of the Douglas Astronomical Society (DAS), which met in the late 1890s. They ultimately became the Manx Astronomical Society (MAS) and were closely linked to the Liverpool Astronomical Society (LAS). The LAS helped establish the British Astronomical Association (BAA), one of the world's leading astronomical organisations. The MAS Journal for 1895/96 features the death of their founder and Vice President Thomas Keig, who was also the first Mayor of Douglas. Until 2011, the Keig family ran a photographic business. Nick Keig, the great-grandson of Thomas, is well known for his sailing exploits.

In 2004 the Douglas Villa Marina entertainment complex reopened after a major refurbishment. The original building had a small domed structure

The Manx and Douglas Astronomical Societies circa 1892.

known as the Mayor's parlour. On the inside of this dome a number of stars had been placed. When I learnt of the plans for the complex, which included the demolition of the Mayor's parlour, I took some photographs of these stars and asked if it would be possible to retain the stars to use them in the IOM Astronomical Society observatory. Unfortunately, this was not possible, and sadly all that remains are a few images.

It is not generally known that the magnificent TT trophies have an astronomical connection. Being the closest planet to the Sun, Mercury is the fastest moving, at an orbital speed of 47.8 km/s (107,082 mph). How appropriate that a depiction of Mercury as the Greek Hermes, the fleet-footed messenger of the Gods, adorns the IOM TT motorcycling trophies.

If we consider the orbital speed of the Earth is 107,208 kmph. (66,660 mph), somewhat faster than the current TT lap record speed of over 217 kmph. (135mph), it would take just over two seconds to travel the distance of the TT course at this speed, assuming it was a straight line!

The Villa Marina, The Mayor's parlour dome.

The exploits of Manx motorcyclist Graham Oates are covered in his book entitled "Aurora to Aerial", another astronomical phenomenon that can be seen in our Dark Manx skies.

In 2019 we commemorated the 50th anniversary of the historic first Moon landing of Apollo 11, which landed on 20th July 1969. This event was the culmination of the goal set by President John F Kennedy on 25th May 1961, when he stated to the US Congress: *"I believe that this nation should commit itself to achieving the goal, before this decade is out, of landing a man on the Moon and returning him safely to Earth".*

While not directly involved in the Isle of Man, several activities and events provide us with links, albeit tenuous, to what has been described as one of the most outstanding achievements of mankind.

The space race started on 4th October 1957 when Sputnik (it was never called Sputnik 1) was launched. The following month, Sputnik 2 was launched. This was spotted in the Manx night sky *(Speyr)* and recorded in the Isle of Man Examiner in November 1957. The report states, *"Sputnik 2 was spotted over Ramsey yesterday; it was due over at 6:40, and dead-on time the satellite sped across the sky. Four men on the Market Square had it in view for several seconds".*

In July 1969, The IOM, along with an estimated 600 million people on Earth, watched avidly and spellbound when Neil Armstrong made that giant

The author with the TT Trophy showing the winged God Mercury.

leap. The IOM Government of the time sent the congratulations of the Manx people to the US. It referred to the fact that this was an important step not just for the American people but also for mankind.

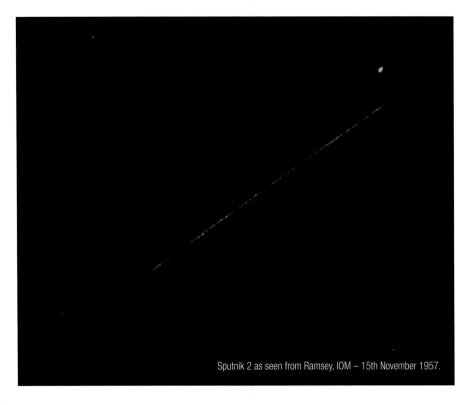

Sputnik 2 as seen from Ramsey, IOM – 15th November 1957.

A few years after the Moon landings, one of the Island's well-known entertainers, the late Laurie Kermode, used to recite a Manx dialect poem entitled:

The Cregneash Apollo Mission
Narrated by Laurie Kermode, Written by Val Hards

"Now word had got down to Rumsaa,
of things goin' on in the South
The Newses was carried by Bridson
Better known as "Billa the mouth"

He tol' of a bloomin big spaceship.,
The lek that had never been seen.
Bein' launched to the Moon from Cregneash boys,
and the skipper'd been named as Cregeen.

Now Cregeen was a man of great knowledge,
He'd travelled to Liverpool twice
He'd been in a real Chinese restaurant
An actually tasted Flied Lice

He picked out his crew which was special
Kelly, Quirk an' Tom Looney from Peel.
The Guv'nor an' all was invited lek,
The Deemsters an' every big Queel

The member for Rushen was honoured
The rocket was his to despatch
He stood there in glory an' revelled
Then he foun' out he hadn't a match

The rocket was lighted at las' boys
After blowin' out two or three times
When the smook cleared away from aroun' them
They watched as the tin monster climbed

Champagne corks was Poppin' all over
An some were full pretty soon
As they waved Cregeen off on his travels
He was headin' direct for the Moon

The ship was goin' well on the two star
Manx Radio was trackin' its path
It was still on its way after two days
An' it had done twenty miles an' a half

At las' came the day of the landin'
The Moon was as clear as a bell
Looney said it looked like a picture
An' Quirk was just frickend to hell

She nosed her away down to the surface,
An' Kelly was yellin' "Manx Rule"
But Cregeen was upset somethin' awful
They'd come down on the top of Barool.

It was great fun to hear Laurie recite the tale of Cregeen and his crew in a distinctive Manx dialect, and it was very popular for many years. It was to be resurrected quite unexpectedly some years later at the opening of the "Mann in Space" exhibition at the House of Manannan in 2004.

There are a few links from the IOM to the Apollo Moon landings. Three of the twelve men who walked on the Moon have walked on the Isle of Man, including Neil Armstrong, who visited on two separate occasions. Armstrong first came to the Island in 1982 and stayed at the Nunnery as a guest of Robert Sangster. Appropriately, the Nunnery became an off-campus centre of the International Space University a few years later.

Sangster also hosted a visit in 1985 of the first US astronaut Alan Shepard, the fifth man to walk on the Moon during the Apollo 14 mission in February 1971. Finally, Jim Irwin, the eighth man to walk on the Moon during the Apollo 15 mission in July 1971, visited the Isle of Man on three occasions. Irwin was accompanied by Al Worden, the Apollo 15 Command Module pilot, on his first visit. During this visit, he planted a tree at Ballakillowey. A plaque nearby commemorates this event.

The International Year of astronomy 2009 logo in English and Manx.

There is a great story regarding Irwin and Worden's visit. While awaiting their flight back home, they went to the Whitestone public house in Ballasalla for a drink, and whilst there, the landlord, Herbie Nelson, asked them where they were from. They replied, *"the USA"*. Herbie also asked them what they did for a living. They replied, *"we're astronauts,"* to which Herbie commented, *"We don't get many astronaut 'fellas' down here in Ballasalla".*

Tree and plaque at
Ballakillowey.

In 2009 the International Astronomical Union (IAU), along with the support of UNESCO, was nominated as the International year of astronomy. In the Isle of Man, we produced our own Manx Gaelic version of the IYA2009 logo.

Also, in 2009, Neil Armstrong returned to the Island as a private guest of well-known resident and inventor John Taylor OBE. Horology was one of Armstrong's interests, so he was fascinated to see some of Johns impressive collection of clocks and watches at Aaragon Mooar in Santon.

Dr John Taylor, Jim Hays and Neil Armstrong at Arragon Mooar,
Santon 18th August 2009. *(John Taylor)*

More recently, in late Victorian times an observatory was established here to enable astronomers to study the stars from the highest point on the Island.

At Snaefell Summit this poster claims there was an observatory at the summit in Victorian times.

Chapter 3

Personal Memories

As a 7-year-old, on Saturday 15th April 1961, I was playing football with some of my friends outside our house in Mossley Hill, Liverpool. We were looking forward to hearing about how our favourite football team, Everton, would get on that afternoon against Cardiff City at Goodison Park in Liverpool. At about 11.00 AM, my mother came outside and said to us, *"Boys come inside and see what is on television"*. We did not want to, but mum went on to say: *"You will want to see this; it's about a man who has just been into space"*. I recall thinking: *"Wow, a man who has been into space!"* We all went in and sat in our lounge. We looked at a small black and white TV screen showing a man in a big coat walking through Red Square in Moscow being greeted by the Soviet Premier Nikita Khrushchev. It was an amazing sight, and it made such an impression on me. My mother was so impressed with this feat that she wrote to the Soviet Embassy in London asking for a photograph of this man, Major Yuri Gagarin, the first man in space. I still have this photograph in my office.

The previous Tuesday, 12th April, Major Yuri Gagarin had flown in his Vostok 1 spacecraft around the Earth in just 108 minutes. The idea of flying in space around the Earth was amazing and fascinating to me in equal measure. This pivotal moment led to my lifelong fascination with spaceflight and astronomy. It turned out it was a great day for another reason, our team managed to beat Cardiff City by five goals to one

Photograph sent to my mother from the Soviet Embassy in London.

Major Gagarin never visited the Isle of Man. However, there is a plaque in Terminal 1 at Manchester airport, marking his visit which can clearly be seen by travellers to and from the Island.

My interest was piqued further just a few weeks later, on 5th May 1961, when the American astronaut Alan Shepard undertook a 15-minute suborbital flight in his Mercury "Freedom 7" spacecraft. In particular, I recall his expressions *"What a beautiful view,"* *"Everything is A-OK"*, *"What a ride"*. It was so exciting for me as a young boy to realise that people could fly into space and come back again. Then just days later, on 25th May, President John F. Kennedy made that famous speech to the US Congress. *"I believe that this nation should commit itself, to achieving the*

YURY GAGARIN
April 12, 1961. The first man in space

YURI GAGARIN
1934 - 1968

Soviet Cosmonaut and first
human to voyage into space

Flew in to Manchester Airport
to be greeted by
thousands of supporters
12th July 1961

Plaque at
Terminal 1,
Manchester airport.

goal, before this decade is out, of landing a man on the Moon and returning him safely to the Earth".

These events in space exploration led to my developing a long-time fascination with the subject. Who could have foreseen that these three events would lead to me travelling the world, lecturing on astronomy and spaceflight on cruise ships? Seeing many wonderful sights, and meeting some amazing people?

As I grew up, I recall many of those first pioneering flights vividly, especially John Glenn's first US orbital flight in his "Friendship 7" spacecraft on 20th February 1962. I was mesmerised by the final Mercury flight in 1963 when Gordon Cooper undertook a 34-hour mission in his "Faith 7" spacecraft. This led to the two-man Gemini missions and another memorable moment for a young keen space enthusiast.

On 21st August 1965, NASA launched the Gemini 5 mission and Gordon Cooper and Pete Conrad spent eight days in orbit. A few days earlier on 18th August 1965, on my twelfth birthday, I was on holiday with my parents in Carbis Bay, St Ives in Cornwall. Unfortunately, I managed to fall down a cliff, and I ended up in hospital for five days. So, when they launched, I had been bed-bound for about three days, and the very idea of spending eight days inside a tiny, weightless capsule was totally abhorrent.

My interest in astronomy and space was reinforced in February 1966. We learned that Jodrell Bank had managed to capture details of a Soviet lunar mission and publicise it before the Soviets could do so. This first-ever "soft" landing on the Moon by Luna 9 was another Soviet first. Upon landing, the spacecraft sent back images of the Lunar surface, and the team at Jodrell Bank intercepted these images. Someone recognised that the image signal was similar to that used by fax machines. Upon request, an appropriate device was loaned to the team from the Daily Express newspaper. It was duly connected, and the images made front pages news the following day. Presumably, this was an irritation to the Soviets. They no doubt had wanted to reveal the images and success of Luna 9 at their own time and convenience.

This was then followed by a persistent and enthusiastic 13-year-old imploring his parents to let him stay up late, to watch Patrick Moore's BBC programme "The Sky at Night". In October 1966, Patrick told us about a possible Leonid meteor storm that may occur on 17th November. Patrick advised viewers to send for a Leonid star chart from the BBC, which I duly did. He also advised us to find a good observing location and look out that evening/early morning for what could be a dramatic display of Leonid meteors. On the evening of Wednesday 16th November, my father took me to Holt's Field in Mossley Hill, Liverpool, near where we lived. We stayed until about 1.00 AM and saw just three faint meteors. They are still marked and timed on my BBC sky at night chart. We learnt the next day that a major display of Leonid's took place over Arizona in the USA. Over 60,000 meteors were seen in under an hour. It was good to hear that the predictions had been correct but so frustrating that we saw so little.

This story was to have an amazing sequel. In October 2018, I had just delivered my Meteors lecture on the cruise ship "Viking Orion". An American lady came up to tell me that her father had taken her to see a meteor storm when she was young. She thought it was in about February 1967. I asked her where she lived then. When she told me that she was living in Arizona, I suggested that she was probably mistaken; it was perhaps four months earlier in November. However, she was astounded when I told her

BBC Sky at Night Leonid shower 1966. Note three marked meteors.

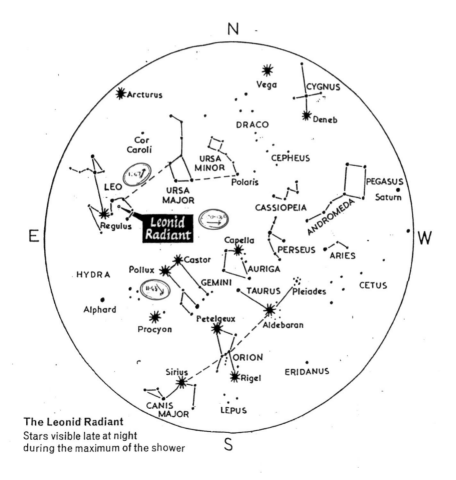

The Leonid Radiant
Stars visible late at night
during the maximum of the shower

that she had almost certainly witnessed the great Leonid meteor "storm" of November 1966. She was the first person I had ever met who had seen this spectacular event. She was surprised that I could pin it down to that exact date. It was such a moving moment for both of us as we recalled the kindness of our two respective fathers.

The following year, 1967, opened sadly. In the UK, we lost Donald Campbell in the Bluebird disaster on Coniston Water on 4th January. This was followed in the US by the horrific launch pad fire at Cape Kennedy on 28th January. This fire took the lives of the Apollo 1 crew of Gus Grissom, Ed White and Roger Chaffee. A faulty wire in the spacecraft caused a fire during a launch simulation test procedure. This disaster led to a significant redesign of the Apollo spacecraft. There then followed another space disaster on 24th April 1967. Soviet cosmonaut Vladimir Komarov perished when his Soyuz spacecraft suffered multiple failures. Upon re-entry, the parachutes failed, and the doomed spacecraft plummeted to the ground. Many thought this might have led to the end of the "Space race" as it became known, but the USA and USSR continued with dogged determination. In October 1968, NASA launched Apollo 7 on a successful test mission that proved the systems and spacecraft. In the meantime, the Soviets' return to flight occurred a few days later when Georgy Beregovoi completed a test flight of the redesigned Soyuz 3 spacecraft.

It was an exciting time, but there was more to come. NASA was making huge strides in the US, but they had a dilemma. They realised that the lunar module would not be ready for its first manned test flight in Earth orbit. It was decided that if the first manned flight of the Apollo 7 spacecraft in October 1968 was successful, then Apollo 8 would be sent on a flight that would orbit the Moon and return. Upon the return of Apollo 7, this audacious plan was confirmed as going ahead. Thus, the stage was set for the first-ever manned mission beyond Earth orbit. On 16th December 1968, the first manned Saturn V rocket with the Apollo 8 spacecraft was launched. Before developing the Saturn series of rockets, all US spacecraft used launch vehicles built and designed for warfare. The various Intercontinental Ballistic missiles (ICBM's) Redstone, Atlas, and Titan missiles were modified and "man-rated" to make them reliable enough to carry astronauts.

On 19th December 1968, I recall sitting at home watching television and the sight and sound of this amazing rocket launching from Florida. Following the launch, the first-ever TLI (trans-lunar injection) took place. The Apollo 8 spacecraft crewed by Frank Borman, Jim Lovell and Bill Anders left Earth orbit bound for the Moon. They successfully entered lunar orbit and read the first few verses of Genesis as they orbited the Moon on Christmas Eve to a spellbound worldwide audience. When the crew returned, the Liverpool Echo newspaper published a multipart series on the flight of Apollo 8 and having obtained multiple copies of the feature. I sent a set off to Frank Borman and his crewmates with a letter of congratulations. You can imagine my delight when I received a signed booklet from Frank. A few weeks later I also received signed photographs from Jim Lovell and Bill Anders.

Fresh from the success of Apollo 8, on 9th January 1969, NASA announced the crew of Apollo 11, which would be the fifth crewed Apollo mission. The crew would comprise Commander Neil Armstrong, Lunar Module Pilot (LMP) Edwin "Buzz" Aldrin and Command Module Pilot (CMP) Michael Collins. If all went as planned with the Apollo 9 and 10 missions, Apollo 11 would be the first mission to attempt a lunar landing. After successfully obtaining autographs from the Apollo 8 crew, I wrote to all three Apollo 11 crew, offering my congratulations and asking for an

Booklet owned by the author and signed by Apollo 8 Cmdr. Frank Borman.

Edwin E. Aldrin, Jr.

Signed Buzz Aldrin photograph received early 1969.

autographed photograph. I was literally over the Moon a few weeks later when I received back from all three their autographs. The one from Buzz was a photograph which had the words *"To Howard Parkin, Thanks for your kind letter, With Best Wishes, Buzz Aldrin, Apollo X1"*. The only problem was that it had been folded in half by the postman to get in our letterbox. This was despite it having "Photograph – Do not Bend" printed on the envelope.

Summer, specifically July, is the time of year when those of us of a certain age recall that first historic Moon landing. On 20th July 1969, Neil Armstrong and Buzz Aldrin landed at Tranquillity base, thus fulfilling President Kennedy's pledge to land on the Moon by the end of the decade. Along with an estimated 600 million people on the Earth, I recall vividly watching the landing, not from the Isle of Man but from another island of the British Isles, the Isle of Wight, where we were on a family holiday. I recall asking my parents to ensure that our holiday cottage had a television to watch this momentous event.

In 2015 I was scheduled to be lecturing on the Cunard cruise ship "Queen Victoria," and Buzz Aldrin was one of the other speakers. He was initially meant to be on board from Los Angeles to New York, and I would be joining the ship at Fort Lauderdale. I took my signed photograph with me. When we embarked in Fort Lauderdale, I immediately went to the Customer Service Desk. I asked if I could leave a message for Colonel Aldrin. I had intended to show him the photograph and show how it had been folded.

CUNARD

QUEEN VICTORIA® 2015 Insights Guest Lecturers

Voyage Number	2015 Dates	Speaker	Expertise
V508	6 - 25 April	Buzz Aldrin	Astronaut
		Bill Miller	Maritime Historian
		Larry Rudner	Panama Canal Expert
		Andy Wyatt	Aviation Expert
V509	25 April - 3 May	Dr. Terry Waite CBE	Hostage Negotiator, Former Hostage, Author & Humanitarian
		Aldon Ferguson	Military Historian
		Howard Parkin	Astronomy and Earth Science
		Simon Dinsdale	Criminology

Queen Victoria lecturers April 2015.

However, I learnt that he had disembarked a few hours previously, so I did not get to meet him!

Mind you, we did get to fly with him. A few years later, when my wife and I returned on a flight from the US into London, there was a sign at the "Meet and Greet" area for Colonel Aldrin. He must have been on our flight, so I can truthfully say I flew with him!

I recall the flights of the remaining Apollo missions quite well, especially the near disaster that was Apollo 13. By the time of the final landing mission of Apollo 17 in December 1972 I was studying to be a teacher at Padgate College, Warrington. It was here that I met my future wife, Sandra, and we both graduated in 1975. We married and set up our home on the Isle of Man. I commenced employment at Heron and Brearley as a Customs and Excise documentation clerk, whilst Sandra eventually became a full-time primary school teacher. I never obtained a full-time teaching post. However, I can claim to have taught continually since 1985, albeit for just 2 hours a week for 12 weeks a year at the IOM College.

Whilst we enjoyed living and working on the Isle of Man, I wondered about the possibility of getting into teaching by offering courses via adult education classes at the IOM College. In early 1985 I made an appointment to see Bev Sharpe, the head of adult education. I had qualified to teach geography and physical education to secondary-aged children. While I realised the latter was unlikely to be an option, I had hoped that teaching geography might have been a possibility. Bev advised that the College adult education department only ran non-vocational subjects such as photography, yoga, playing the guitar, etc. He asked if I had any hobbies or interests that I could teach, to which I replied that I was interested in astronomy. With Halley's Comet *(Comaid Halley)* predicted to be visible later in 1985 and 1986, I could possibly talk about that. Bev replied, *"that's perfect; it's topical and just what we are looking for".*

In September 1985, the IOM College adult education department prospectus offered a new course to Manx residents, "An Introduction to Astronomy". I realised I needed to do some preparatory work, and I purchased several books on the subject. That August, we were down in Falmouth on holiday. We visited a shop called Trago Mills where I saw a book entitled "The Practical Astronomer," by Colin A. Ronan. Unfortunately, they only had a store copy left. When I came home, I wrote to them and explained why I wanted it and asked if I could purchase a copy of it. I was delighted when I received a copy of the book direct from them. It happened to be a copy one of the staff had purchased, but they let me have it as they felt my need was greater than theirs. I always remember that kindness. It was a book I was to use extensively in the first few years I was teaching at the IOM College.

Halley's Comet was a big disappointment in 1985/86 as it was on the far side of the Sun at its closest approach to the Earth. Still, it was very newsworthy, and I was able to talk about it at length, and it got me into teaching and lecturing on the subject.

At this time, little was I to realise it would lead me to meet one of the world's most prominent theoretical physicists and cosmologists, Professor Stephen Hawking. In 1985 one of my first ever IOM College students, Dr John Taylor, the inventor and horologist, told me he was disappointed with "the comet". But years later, John kindly invited me to meet Professor Hawking when he visited John at his home Aaragon Mooar, at Santon in 2012.

A few years later, I also joined him on his private plane on a flight to see all five planets in the morning sky in January 2016.

In my teaching, I quickly realised that my knowledge was somewhat limited and I had to undertake a good deal of reading and research, so, I enrolled with the Open University to do a degree course. In 1994 I graduated with a Bachelor of Science degree (BSc). A few years later, in 1996, I applied for and obtained a position as the Public Services manager with MNH, a post for which being a graduate was a pre-requisite.

In 1989 we had a family holiday in Florida. I managed to obtain press accreditation and had a VIP tour of the Kennedy Space Center by NASA's

The author with Stephen Hawking and at Aaragon Mooar, Isle of Man – 18th August 2012.

Discovery in the Orbiter Processing Facility at the KSFC.

Manny Virata. The highlight of my visit was when Manny showed me around the Orbiter Processing Facility, which at that time had the Space Shuttle Discovery inside. I was allowed to walk around and underneath Discovery, and it was a fantastic experience. I was able to inspect the area around the undercarriage. At the time, we did not know that it was damage close to this area that led to the loss of the Shuttle Challenger and its crew in 2001.

In 1989 a few years after I commenced teaching at the IOM College, a notice appeared in the the IOM Examiner newspaper from Gary Kewin asking if anyone one was interested in starting up a local astronomy society. On 29th May, a group of us met at the Creg ny Baa Hotel and the Isle of Man Astronomical Society (IOMAS) was established.

A few weeks later, on 6th July, I gave a talk for the Society entitled "The 20th anniversary of the Apollo 11 mission". I recall placing a slide projector on the snooker table, which we then all had to sit around. Shortly after, the premises closed for refurbishment, and we moved to the Falcon Cliff Hotel. We met there until 1993, and then we had to move again when they closed for conversion into offices. We moved to the club room downstairs at the Quarterbridge Hotel, where we met until it closed due to flooding in 1994. Undeterred, we moved to the Manx Automobile Club in Hill Street, Douglas. In July 1994, I gave another talk, this time entitled "25 years since Apollo 11". We eventually moved out of the Auto Club in December 2001, when we moved to our new Observatory in Foxdale.

In 1990, through my lecturing at the IOM College, I managed to secure a loan of some Moonrock samples from the Apollo missions through the Particle Physics and Astronomy Research Council (PPARC) in the UK, now

Patrick Moore and the author at the Manx Museum – November 1992.

known as the Science Technology Facilities Council (SRFC). They still have one of the coolest astronomical addresses, Polaris House, North Star Avenue. The loan arrangements were rigorous. The samples had to be delivered to the Island by a PPARC courier. They had to be kept in a safe with very stringent security specifications. On the night that the samples arrived, I had to go to College and ensure they were placed in an appropriate safe. As I drove home that night along Glencrutchery Road, the Moon was rising. It was an inspiring and memorable moment.

Such was the interest in these unique samples, I took them to several IOM Schools, talked about them, and showed them to the pupils. One of them, Murrays Junior Road in Douglas, invited me to bring them to show a particular class. When I arrived, I was escorted into the hall, and the whole school of about 350 pupils were there!

The IOMAS held a star party in 1991 at Nairbyl when I saw my first-ever display of the Northern Lights. In 1995, we had a star party at the summit of Snaefell. Little did we realise at the time that we would return for the many "Pie in the sky" events 15 years later.

Patrick Moore at Laxey Wheel with members of the IOM Astronomical Society – November 1992.

In November 1992, the IOMAS invited Sir Patrick Moore FRAS over to the Island. Patrick had an affinity for the Island, having flown into Jurby

during World War II. I collected him from Ronaldsway Airport to take him to the Sefton Hotel. As we drove down Richmond Hill, he saw the bright lights from Ballakinnish nurseries at the foot of the hill. He turned to me and exclaimed, *"Good God, what's that!"*

We took him to the Sefton Hotel. Whilst he was registering, someone had written "astrologer" as his profession. He immediately crossed this out and replaced it with "astronomer!"

The following day, we took him on a tour of the Island. This included the Steam Railway workshops, the Camera Obscura, Laxey Wheel, Odin's Raven and Jurby. That evening, we held a celebratory dinner (with Patrick as our guest of honour). The following day he gave a fascinating public lecture at the Manx Museum. Following his visit, the Society was honoured when he agreed to become the IOM Astronomical Societies Patron, a post he held until his death in December 2012.

One of my most amusing teaching memories occurred in 1992. One of my class, Lee, a primary school teacher, asked me if I could think of a prank she could use as an April Fool's day gag for her class. After some

The IOM Astronomical Society Observatory at Foxdale.

consideration, I came up with an idea. I suggested she told her class that the NASA Space Shuttle, Atlantis (Mission STS 45), would be flying over the IOM on the morning of Wednesday, 1st April. The crew wanted Isle of Man residents to help them. They had onboard a new, special type of camera. They wanted to test out its resolution as they flew over the Island that morning. The weather conditions were irrelevant as it was designed to penetrate cloud cover. The day arrived, and the headteacher announced this "event" at the morning assembly. Just before the designated time, the whole school went outside. They even wrote "hello" using crash mats in the playground. The time duly arrived, and they all waved. Only then did the headteacher ask them all, *"what day is it?"* There was an unexpected sequel to this story. In about 2009, we had a student, Suzie, working with us at the Manx Museum on a work experience. Whilst chatting, Suzie told me about a prank played on her and the whole of Ballasalla school back in April 1992.

In 1996, Dr Henry Soper, a renowned amateur astronomer who lived in Maughold, offered to sell the Society some land in Foxdale, where he previously had an observatory. Following the purchase, we set about obtaining funds to build our own Observatory. At one of our monthly meetings at the Manx Automobile Club, a new member Colin Hill stated that he would consider building an observatory for us. Colin had famously hit the headlines a few years previously when he took a suitcase of money to the "Thrust" world speed record team in the US when they were running out of funds. Colin felt we were also a deserving cause. We spoke in more detail to him about the project. He realised that our plans were realistic and feasible and we mutually agreed to proceed. We submitted plans, obtained planning permission, and started the preparatory work. In May 1999, the prefabricated Observatory arrived and was erected on

Showing diners, the stars during a Pie in the sky event on Snaefell summit.

site. In January 2002, we held our first meeting at the premises. I was delighted when I was invited to be the first speaker at the IOM Astronomical Society Observatory.

We then set about raising funds for a telescope. Eventually, we installed a 16-inch Meade ETX 16 Cassegrain telescope at the Observatory in June 2003.

Since then, the Society has grown from strength to strength. We have hosted dozens of visits by schools, youth groups and various adult organisations to the observatory and have on many occasions managed to show our visitors some of the features of our Manx Dark skies. In 2010, following the successful "2009 International Year of Astronomy", the IOMAS, in conjunction with IOM Railways (IOMR), commenced the "Pie in the Sky" events.

For these events, members of the public purchased tickets for a trip to the summit of Isle of Man's only mountain Snaefell, on the Victorian Snaefell Mountain Railway. At the summit, a meal comprising meat pie and a dessert

The Starlight Express – January 2021. (Rob Farrington)

of apple pie was served. There then followed a talk by either me or another Society member. If clear, the diners would have an opportunity to observe the Manx night sky from the Islands closest place to space.

Up to six sessions were held each year, usually to a sell-out audience of up to 80 guests per night. These brought in invaluable funds for the Society.

Coinciding with the BBC Stargazing Live series on Television in 2014, the Society arranged a stargazing session at the Nobles Park Dark Sky Site in Douglas. We subsequently moved this event to Onchan Park, another of the Islands Dark Sky Sites. The Society, in recent years has also held an annual star party in Ballaugh, in the north of the Island.

Following the Covid crisis in 2020, it was not possible to continue these popular events, but in January 2021, a "Starlight Express" trip on the Isle of Man Railways (IMR) Steam train was held. Several members and over 70 guests travelled to Poulson Park in Castletown, one of the IOM's 26 Dark Sky Discovery Sites (see chapter six). During the trip guests enjoyed an excellent meal. It was a spectacularly clear night, and we had a successful stargazing session looking at many features of the winter sky. After about an hour we were summoned back to the train by the train's whistle. Surely a unique occurrence in the world of stargazing?

Chapter 4

The Isle of Man in Space

In 1998, Chris Stott (Astronaut Nicole's husband) established ManSat, a private company owned and registered in the Isle of Man. Through ManSat, Chris made a proposal to the Isle of Man Government suggesting that the Island ought to consider becoming a player in the world of space commerce by becoming involved in satellite orbital filing. This is where an individual nation, such as the Isle of Man, can have regulated access to the radio spectrum necessary to operate and use satellites in space.

In 2000, following detailed discussions, the Island agreed with ManSat to provide secure and reliable access to the orbital filing process for satellite operators via the Isle of Man. Drawing from the many additional financial and regulatory advantages the Isle of Man has to offer in the world of international finance, the IOM Government "Space Isle" initiative was established.

As a consequence of this initiative, several leading satellite companies established a presence on the Island. These included SES, Inmarsat, Telesat, Loral Skynet, Viasat, Sea launch, and ManSat. This led to the Isle of Man achieving a role and position as one of the world leaders in the administration of commercial space exploration, providing expert advice and support for the rapidly growing commercial aspects of the space industry. In August 2010, industry analyst "Ascend" ranked the Isle of Man as the fifth most likely nation to get its flag upon the Moon. The Island was

IOM Courier from
22nd June 2012.

ranked as 50 to 1 to win the new Moon race behind just the USA, Russia, China and India.

In 2003 the British Astronomical Association (BAA) accepted an Isle of Man Astronomical Society invitation to hold their 2004 annual "Out-of-London" meeting on the Isle of Man. As a result, a series of lectures was planned for delivery at the Manx Museum in September 2004, including one by myself and several social events.

In 1995 NASA's Galileo spacecraft entered into orbit around Jupiter. It was to remain operating in the Jovian environment until 2003. Amongst the thousands of images taken by the spacecraft were a number of the surface of Europa, one of Jupiter's Galilean Moons. Europa is of great interest to astronomers. It is believed that Europa may have an ocean underneath its icy surface. NASA proposed that larger craters and features on the surface would be named after Celtic and Gaelic Gods and Deities. One crater was named Manannan. There are many myths and legends about Manannan, and some scholars claim it was Manannan that gave the Isle of Man its name.

A few years earlier, NASA had announced that it was considering sending an unmanned spacecraft to Europa, one of Jupiter's moons. The spacecraft would land, and drill through its icy crust and explore the ocean believed to exist under the ice. The proposed landing site was to be the "*Manx crater*" Manannan.

In my role at MNH, it was agreed that an invitation by the BAA to the House of Manannan visitor centre in Peel by the BAA would be appropriate. I was chatting with Chris Stott sometime later. He asked if MNH would be interested in having a piece of Moonrock loaned from NASA on display in the House of Manannan for the BAA visit. This offer was readily and

The crater Manannan on Jupiter's Moon Europa. *(NASA)*

The House of Manannan exhibition graphic "From the Viking Kingdom to the Space Kingdom".

Chris Stott and the author with the Apollo 15 moonrock sample.

gratefully accepted by MNH and the proposed Moonrock loan and associated exhibition went ahead.

Our BAA delegates were most impressed with the exhibition, as were many thousands of other visitors. The sample, a fist-sized chunk, was significantly larger than the samples I had obtained on loan previously in 1990 for my IOM College courses. It was initially intended that the sample would come from the Apollo 17 mission, but at the last minute, this was changed to a sample from the Apollo 15 mission. This turned out to be fortuitous.

At Easter 2004, I was on holiday in Florida and visited the Kennedy Space Flight Center (KSFC). Whilst there, I met former astronaut Al Worden (the CMP from Apollo 15). As we chatted, he fondly recalled his visit to the Isle of Man. He was intrigued to learn that a piece of Moonrock collected by his colleagues during the Apollo 15 mission in 1972 was to be displayed on the Isle of Man later that year.

One of my fondest memories of the House of Manannan Moonrock exhibition was the opening event. To commemorate this special occasion, we invited the late Manx entertainer Laurie Kermode to recite the "Cregneash Apollo mission," as detailed in chapter two.

"International Space Day" commemorates annually the launch on 4th October 1957 of Sputnik, the first artificial Earth satellite. On this date in 2008, the Strasbourg based International Space University International (ISU) opened the Institute of Space Commerce at the Nunnery Campus in the Isle of Man. The opening event was attended by many dignitaries, including Michael Potter of the ISU, George Abbey, former Director of the NASA Johnson Spaceflight Center and space tourist So-Yeon Yi from South Korea, the second Asian woman to travel into space.

Later that year, we were delighted to learn from Chris that Nicole had been allocated her first space mission. Launching as a mission specialist on the STS 128 mission on the Space Shuttle Discovery in August 2009. Nicole

Apollo 15 CMP Al Worden and the author at KSFC – 2004.

was to serve as a flight engineer for three months onboard the ISS.

A few months before the launch, Chris contacted me and advised that all astronauts undertaking their first flight can have an unofficial "Ground crew". This "crew" could contribute to the astronauts chosen charity and obtain a unique T-shirt. Several IOMAS members ordered some of the T-shirts, and Chris asked us to have a picture taken of us wearing them at a Manx landmark that he would show Nicole. So, at our Observatory one

The author with Ian Jarritt of ManSat and Laurie Kermode at the House of Manannan.

The Institute of Space Commerce at the Nunnery, Douglas, Isle of Man.

Nicole's IOMAS
Ground crew.

Saturday morning, we had a "team photograph" taken, wearing our special T-shirts, holding an Isle of Man Astronomical Society banner, and a Manx and US flag.

The mission successfully launched on 28th August 2009. A few weeks later, I was delighted to receive an email from Nicole onboard the ISS. When I opened it, there was a copy of our "team photograph" in an ISS window. We held the IOMAS AGM later that week, and I managed to keep it a secret from our members until I showed it at the meeting.

It was met with gasps of astonishment and applause from all present. Amongst Nicole's many awards is one from the IOMAS. Her photograph

Nicole's IOMAS
Ground Support
Crew, in the window
of the ISS. *(NASA)*

won the 2008 IOMAS photograph of the year trophy. A few weeks later, on 16th October, the "live link" took place at the Manx Museum.

During Nicole's time "on station," I was across in the UK visiting my brother Graham and his wife Hiliary in North Wales. He asked me all about Nicole's flight and the live link, so I decided to play a trick on him. There used to be a group of satellites (Iridium satellites) with large solar panels which caught the sunlight. Consequently, these can produce a flare that could be seen very brightly from specific areas on the Earth. These "Iridium flares" could be very precisely timed and were very noticeable. One evening I was out with my brother, and I knew exactly when and where there would be an Iridium flare that evening. I told him to look at a specific part of the sky at the appropriate time. The flare appeared, and Graham turned to me, astonished and asked me, "*What the **** was that?*" I told him I had asked Nicole to "flash the lights" on the ISS. He just looked at me incredulously and was genuinely amazed, that was until I started laughing! I just could not keep my face straight.

Originally Nicole was to have returned from her mission to Russia on the Soyuz TMA 15 mission, but this was changed for operational reasons. Nicole eventually returned to Earth on 28th November 2009 on the Space Shuttle Atlantis. During her mission Nicole undertook a six and half hour spacewalk. She captured a Japanese cargo vehicle with the ISS's remote manipulator arm. Nicole also became the first NASA astronaut to be

Orion and the ISS (over Laxey Wheel – October 2009. *(Pete Geddes)*

allocated another flight whilst in orbit during the mission.

Nicole's second mission was again on Space Shuttle Discovery, this time on the STS 133 mission. This was a 13-day flight. It was initially scheduled to be the Space Shuttle's final mission. Subsequently, flights of Endeavour (STS 134) and Atlantis (STS 135) took place following STS 133. Sandra and I were delighted to receive an invitation to the launch, scheduled for 1st November. We travelled to Florida and attended Nicole's pre-launch party at the KSFC. We met several astronauts, including Mike Good. He had been one of the spacewalkers during the Hubble Space Telescope servicing mission in 2009. I recall Mike telling me that: *"I was just a repairman"*.

I also met another spacewalker Steve Bowen who became a late addition to the STS 133 crew, replacing Tim Kopra following a cycling accident. Tim eventually flew again to the ISS with British Astronaut Tim Peake in 2015.

Unfortunately, the first launch attempt on 1st November and four further attempts were postponed. Sandra and I managed to stay over through to the attempt on the 5th November, but the problems identified during this attempt led to the whole launch vehicle and attached Shuttle being returned to the vast Vehicle Assembly Building (VAB) for repairs before finally launching on 26th February 2011. However, we did manage to get out to the

Hubble repairman Mike Good, Gary Corlett and the author.

launch pad on the evening of the 4th November to see Discovery prior to fuelling for the following mornings' launch attempt.

With Sandra at the launch pad (above left) and (above right) Chris Stott and the author at the launch pad.

Following the mission, the Isle of Man Government invited the STS 133 crew and their families to attend the 2012 Tynwald day ceremony. During their visit, the crew undertook a lecture at the Villa Marina with Professor Brian Cox for some of the Island's sixth form students. A few months later, when Professor Cox spoke in New York, he advised he had been particularly impressed with the questions and level of the Manx students' knowledge. The interest in space, astronomy and the associated sciences is very high on the Island. Chris Stott's Company ManSat sponsors three Manx schoolchildren each year to attend a NASA "Space school" in Houston, Texas and also sponsors Manx teams entering the "Conrad Spirit of Innovation Challenge". This is a global business challenge for high schools created by the late Apollo 12 Astronaut Pete Conrad's "Conrad Foundation". In 2014 a team from the QE2 High School in Peel won a place in the semi-final in this prestigious competition. Island school children have also been involved in the "Space launch challenge". This is a competition in which the Island's secondary school pupils design and launch model rockets

On 2nd July 2012, The Isle of Man Astronomical Society was honoured to have as their guests at the observatory four of the STS 133 crew, NASA astronauts Nicole Stott, Eric Boe, Mike Barrett, and Steve Bowen.

During the visit, the crew presented the Society with a montage of images from Discovery's final voyage. The Society presented Chris with a birthday cake suitably decorated with a satellite and a shuttle. Nicole was also presented by Society membership secretary Dave Storey with a series of Discovery and ISS images in the skies over the Observatory, taken by Dave during the mission. At one point during the evening, although it was still broad daylight, I advised that the planet Saturn was visible in the observatories 16-inch telescope. We all had to step aside quickly to avoid

Mike Barrett, Eric Boe, Nicole Stott, the author and Steve Bowen at the IOMASO.

being crushed by four keen astronauts/astronomers and their families as they made their way up to the telescope. We now know first-hand just how fit NASA astronauts are. During their visit to the Island, the crew also took the opportunity to visit many of the Island's attractions and met key members of the thriving Manx aerospace industry.

There was a great Manx sequel to their visit. One of the crew, Mike Barrett, was fascinated by the Great Laxey Wheel, the "Lady Isabella". He broadcast all about it on his return to the US in the "Engines of our Ingenuity" series produced by Houston Public Media. This is broadcast on the US public radio network.

Nicole retired from NASA in July 2015 and is now heavily involved as a space artist and in numerous outreach projects. In May/June 2016, an exhibition of her work was held at the Sayle Gallery in Douglas.

Both Chris and Nicole are regular visitors to the Island and are very supportive of Island events and activities. In November 2020, I once again hosted another "live link" with Nicole, this time with three primary schools celebrating 20 years of the continued occupation of the International Space Station.

In 2010 "Excalibur Almaz" established a presence on the Island to promote space tourism. The Company purchased two Russian space stations, other components and three Almaz three-seat capsules. The intention was

Mike Reynolds, Nicole Stott, Eric Boe, Mike Barrett, Steve Bowen and
the author at Laxey Wheel during the STS 133 crew visit 2012.

Sandra, Nicole and the author at
the Sayle Gallery – June 2016.

An Excalibur Almaz spacecraft showing the Manx three legs.

to refurbish this equipment and provide fare-paying passengers access to an orbiting Excalibur-Almaz 29-ton space station. The concept was that using equipment that had been flown and proven previously would save significant development costs estimated at two billion dollars. However, the rise of other commercial spacecraft initiatives such as Virgin Galactic, SpaceX, Blue Origins and others has led to a mothballing of these exciting

IOMAS members with cosmonaut Valeri Tokarev (4th from right).

The optics for this laser were made in Onchan, Isle of Man

plans. However, Excalibur Almaz still maintains a presence on the Island. At the time of writing, two of the Excalibur Almaz capsules are on the Island, one at Castle Rushen High school in Castletown. The other capsule, together with the Excalibur Almaz space station, is on display at the Isle of Man Motor Museum in Jurby.

In 2009 NASA's Phoenix lander on Mars discovered snow in the Martian atmosphere using a Light Detection and Ranging system (LiDAR) developed in Onchan, Isle of Man by optical Company, CVI, Melles-Griot.

In 2011, SES, a leading satellite launch company with a presence on the Island since 2004, became the main sponsor of the Zero TT motorcycle race. In 2012 the first 100 mph average lap on an electric motorcycle was achieved. Other industries working within the sector include several precision optical companies, including SLS Optics and Manx Precision Optics.

In recent years, many planets have been discovered orbiting distant stars. These planets are called "exoplanets". The IAU have the responsibility for naming and defining all astronomical objects. It was the IAU that downgraded Pluto to "dwarf" planetary status in 2006. As part of their centenary celebrations in 2019, they launched a worldwide competition, the

Phoenix Lander on Mars. *(NASA)*

The start of a "Zero TT" race.

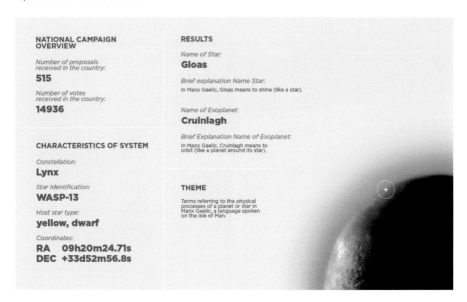

NATIONAL CAMPAIGN OVERVIEW

Number of proposals received in the country:
515

Number of votes received in the country:
14936

CHARACTERISTICS OF SYSTEM

Constellation:
Lynx

Star Identification:
WASP-13

Host star type:
yellow, dwarf

Coordinates:
**RA 09h20m24.71s
DEC +33d52m56.8s**

RESULTS

Name of Star:
Gloas

Brief explanation Name Star:
In Manx Gaelic, Gloas means to shine (like a star).

Name of Exoplanet:
Cruinlagh

Brief Explanation Name of Exoplanet:
In Manx Gaelic, Cruinlagh means to orbit (like a planet around its star).

THEME

Terms referring to the physical processes of a planet or star in Manx Gaelic, a language spoken on the Isle of Man.

IAU announcement of Manx names Gloas and Cruinlagh.

"NameExoWorlds" project. The IAU took 100 unnamed stars and planets and invited 100 countries to name a specific exoplanet and its parent star. The UK was allocated a star (WASP-13) in the constellation of Lynx: The Cat. It is faint with a magnitude of +10.42. Well below naked-eye visibility. The planet allocated was at that time known as WASP 13b. As the IOM is not part of the UK, a Manx primary school, Cronk y Berry wrote and obtained permission to submit an entry to name the UK designated star and the associated planet.

Of 515 entries, which were then shortlisted to 12, a public vote was then held to find a winner. From just under 15,000 votes cast, the Cronk y Berry school entry was voted the winner. The IAU website reports that the chosen names "refer to the physical processes of a planet or star in Manx Gaelic". The star is named "Gloas," which in Manx Gaelic means shine (like a star) and the planet is named "Cruinlagh," which in Manx Gaelic means to orbit (like a planet around its star).

It was appropriate that the winning entry from the Isle of Man should be for a star and planet in the constellation of Lynx: The Cat, which was portrayed as a Manx tailless cat in the Millennium stamp issue (Chapter 5).

While many of the space industry players have now moved on to other jurisdictions and initiatives, it is estimated that the Isle of Man's space sector contributed well over £27M in direct exchequer benefit to the Isle of Man Government during the last 20 years. For some time, the Island had a significant global space sector profile. It was represented at many of the main satellite and commercial "new space" events worldwide.

In July 2021, the Isle of Man Government formally accepted NASA's

Artemis Accords. Chief Minister Howard Quayle MHK said: "*The Isle of Man Government has always been supportive of the Island's diversified economy, including business that undertakes space related activities. The Government supports the principles of the Accords, which build on existing international obligations that apply to the Island, and their extension will benefit relevant Island businesses by ensuring that they are able to participate fully in activities of the Artemis programme.*"

Later in July 2021, it was announced that the Isle of Man Government had agreed with Starlink, the space internet service created in 2015 by Elon Musk's space transportation firm SpaceX, to set up a "ground station" on the Island in the Irish Sea to provide internet access from satellites in low Earth orbit to homes and offices.

A spokesperson for the Island's Department for Enterprise confirmed, "*This is very exciting and positive news for the Island which will enable the deployment of satellite broadband service on-Island and further afield.*"

In 2001, following a deal between the Russian MirCorp and US-based Space Adventures, Dennis Tito visited the ISS for seven days in April–May, becoming the world's first "fee-paying" space tourist. Tito paid a reported $20 million for his trip. This was followed by six others, including South African and Manx resident Mark Shuttleworth and fellow space tourist So-Yeon Yi from South Korea, who visited the IOM in 2008.

Twenty years later, in 2021, a new era of space exploration began with the launch of several commercial human spaceflights. In July, Richard Branson and Jeff Bezos from Virgin Galactic and Blue Origin, respectively, flew into space on suborbital flights. In September, the Inspiration4 mission successfully took place with a crew comprising billionaire Jared Isaacman and three "ordinary citizens" on a three-day mission in a SpaceX Dragon spacecraft. In October, a Russian film director and actor are visiting the ISS. The Axiom organisation are planning their first mission to the ISS with SpaceX in early 2022 with the long-term goal of establishing a private space station, and SpaceX are also planning a private lunar flyby mission in 2023. At the same time, NASA is progressing with their Artemis programme, including the new SLS launch system and their new Orion spacecraft. In addition, the Russian and Chinese space agencies are moving forward with their own national programmes. The future of human space flight, not just into Earth orbit but to the Moon and beyond, is very exciting and it is undoubtedly only a matter of time before we get a Manx born astronaut into space.

Chapter 5

IOM Post Office Space Stamps

In 1997, having obtained my Science degree, I changed career and became the Public Services Manager for MNH. This brought me into contact with many different organisations and people working in the tourism and hospitality sectors. Amongst my new contacts was the Isle of Man Post Office Philatelic Bureau.

Since its inauguration in 1973 as an entity separate from the UK Post Office, the Isle of Man Postal authority, now known as IOM Post, made a conscious decision to utilise the unique nature of the authority to set up the IOM Philatelic Bureau. The Bureau had a remit to issue special stamps to commemorate events and activities not just from and about the Isle of Man but also including events of worldwide significance.

In August 1998, after several successful space-related issues, The Bureau Manager, Dot Tilbury, contacted me and asked whether I could develop an astronomical theme for a Manx Millennium issue. In particular, they wanted something special for what would hopefully be a unique Isle of Man issue. They intended to market such an issue worldwide to mark the dawn of the new Millennium. Strictly speaking, using the Gregorian calendar, the new Millenium began on 1st January 2001, but IOM Post, along with most of the popular media chose to celebrate a year earlier.

I looked into the idea and identified that most westerly and easterly locations of the Isle of Man at sea level would be at the Sound and Maughold Head, respectively. From these locations, the last sunset of 1999 and the first sunrise of 2000 would occur. Using these locations would be unmistakably Manx and could form the basis of a set of unique stamps. I discussed this idea with the Bureau, they liked the idea and agreed that both sites would be very suitable. However, they wanted a set of at least three stamps. They asked me to think about ideas for a second and possibly third stamp, assuming the first and last would be using the Sound and Maughold, respectively. I eventually came up with a concept that ultimately became a very successful issue for the IOM Post Office Philatelic Bureau.

Every location on the planet has its own particular zenith, the point directly overhead. Such zeniths can be considered unique to a specific geographical location. So, the Isle of Man would have its own distinctive millennium zenith. With this in mind, we could identify the actual point directly overhead at the stroke of midnight on 31st December 1999. My original thought was to determine which star was closest to what I started calling the "Manx Millennium Zenith" or MMZ.

I looked at various books, charts and computer programmes, including my Norton's Star Atlas that I had bought as a keen teenager in Liverpool in the 1960s. I quickly realised that there was no bright star anywhere near the MMZ, but the MMZ was just inside the border of the constellation Lynx: The Cat. One of the most distinctive Manx icons known worldwide is the famous tail-less Manx cat. How appropriate the MMZ was just within the borders of a celestial cat.

I was pretty excited about this "discovery", but I wanted to be 100 per cent certain. So, I contacted the IOMAS Patron and well-known astronomer Patrick Moore. I asked him if he could confirm that the MMZ was within the constellation of Lynx. I was delighted to learn from Patrick that I was correct. So, I started working on some initial concepts and designs

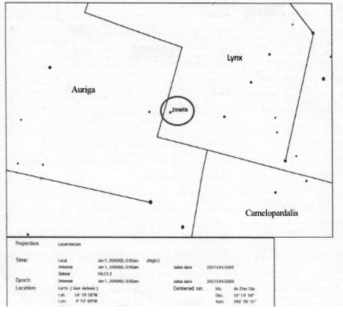

Location of the Manx Millenium Zenith inside boundary of constellation of Lynx: The Cat.

I presented my findings to the Philatelic Bureau. In addition, I produced a mock-up of the three stamps, showing the various constellations and features on each proposed stamp.

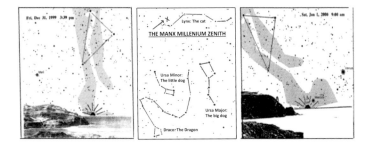

My original designs of the Manx Millenium Midnight stamps.

I also included the asterism (page 197) of the "Summer Triangle," which would appear on the first and last stamps. The midnight stamp would show the constellations of Ursa Major: The Great Bear, Ursa Minor: The Little Bear, Lynx: The Cat and Draco: The Dragon and another asterism known as "The Plough" *(Arc ny Twoaie)*. The inclusion of Draco caused quite a spark of interest at the Post Office because the year 2000 was the Chinese Year of the Dragon. One of the major markets for IOM stamps is the Far East, so we agreed to include this as another distinctive element. We then set about having the artwork and design drawn up. My original design had a standing Manx cat, but this was changed to show a crouching Manx cat, which did look more effective.

I suggested that the Post Office asked Patrick Moore to endorse the issue, and we were delighted when he agreed to do so. Then, with my IOMAS hat on, I suggested that we could also ask if Patrick would sign some of the covers. We could then sell these to raise funds for the Society who wanted to buy a telescope at the Society's Observatory in Foxdale.

Once the covers were produced, I sent one hundred of them to Patrick. He duly signed them and sent them back. However, a problem emerged. When they came back, they had rubbed together, and Patrick's signature was smudged and had completely rubbed off on about 40 of them. But as only Patrick could do, when I told him, he just said, "*just send them again*". When they came back, this time they were fine, and as a consequence, we raised over £1000 for the IOMAS telescope fund.

Before the actual production of the stamps, I was asked to write the accompanying notes, which would be inserted into the envelope for each first-day cover. I had for some time been following the launch and

 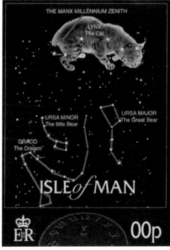

The first and final design showing a Manx Cat at the MMZ.

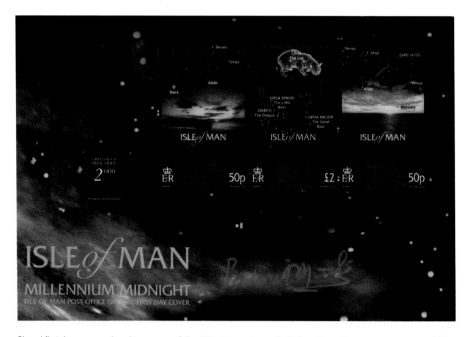

Signed first day cover of the Manx Millennium issue.

development of the ISS. It was intended that this orbiting outpost would be manned for the first time sometime in the year 2000. With this in mind, I had the artist insert an ISS orbital track on the final design of the Maughold Head stamp. I was delighted but somewhat relieved when the first crew took up occupation of the ISS in November 2000. My last comment in the text was to use Frank Borman's words from that famous Apollo 8 Christmas broadcast about *"all of us on the good Earth"*.

The stamps, first-day covers and presentation packs were launched just before midnight on the 31st December 1999. The stamps were a great success worldwide, and the third stamp was to be re-issued a year later.

Following the Manx Millennium midnight issue, I was again approached by the Bureau in mid-2000 and asked, *"How can we follow up the success of the Millennium issue?"* I suggested that we could do something linked to the film *"2001: A Space Odyssey"*. The film had been released in 1968. It had been directed by Stanley Kubrick, and the screenplay was written by Arthur C Clarke. The ability to predict the future of space travel and space exploration by Sir Arthur (he was knighted in 1998) had made him a household name. It was Sir Arthur who, in 1945 in "Wireless World" magazine, had suggested that an artificial satellite in a geostationary orbit could be used for worldwide communication. Today this orbit is known universally as "the Clarke orbit". This immediately piqued the Bureau's interest, and we discussed the way forward. I proposed that the third stamp from the millennium series could be used, as it was this one that took us into the twenty-first century. Many ideas and suggestions were considered, and we finally settled on a design.

A few days later, whilst talking with Chris Stott, he advised that he had met Sir Arthur in Sri Lanka some years previously. So, on behalf of IOM Post, Chris contacted Sir Arthur and asked if he would kindly consider being involved in the issue. Sir Arthur, who had previously worked as a postman in Somerset, readily agreed to endorse the issue. He signed several covers and wrote some words entitled *"A thousand years hence"* for Isle of Man Post, an extract of which is detailed below:

"...the exploration of the Solar system will be the main business of the next Millennium...I would like to close with what is one of the future's most awesome possibilities – that some people alive today may witness the year 3000. This may be through the achievement of biological immortality, 'downloading' the mind into another carrier (probably inorganic) or suspended animation".

Sir Arthur died in 2008, but his words are thought-provoking and prophetic, as were his many novels.

The 2001 first-day cover was released on 1st January 2001, but this was not the last time we would use the film *"2001 A Space Odyssey"* for philatelic purposes in the Isle of Man. In 2018 to commemorate 50 years since the film's release, a new set of stamps was issued.

In 2003, the IOM Post office issued a new space issue, which

IOM Post 2001 First Day cover signed by Arthur C Clarke and Katharina Kubrick.

commemorated the work of a range of Manx companies involved in space exploration and development. This issue, "Mann in Space," featured the work of ManSat, Sea Launch, and Loral Skynet and utilised the talents of renowned space artists Robert McCall and Eric Gignac, commemorating the Island's links with the space community.

I wrote the filler card for the fifth stamp by McCall in this issue named "The Arrival". For this first-day cover, Robert McCall wrote:

"The future is bright and filled with promise for all of us and the human spirit driven as it is with the insatiable desire to explore and to understand, will continue forever to reach upward and outward".

This particular stamp highlighted the role of ManSat, who had recently inaugurated an annual scholarship scheme as part of their outreach programme for Manx students to attend a residential week in the USA at "Space School."

As we approached the 40th anniversary of Apollo 11, the first lunar landing mission, IOM Post, through Chris and Nicole Stott, made contact with Alan (Al) Bean, the fourth man to have walked on the Moon during the Apollo 12 mission in November 1969. Al Bean flew twice in space – to the Moon on Apollo 12 and on the second Skylab mission in 1973. He retired from NASA in 1981 and became a space artist. Al's paintings are literally "out of this world". He included tiny fragments of lunar soil from his spacesuit in each of his creations. He also added tiny fragments of the US flag from the Apollo 12 mission patch and some foil from the spacecraft's hatch.

A second "Mann in space" issue was issued on 12th April 2009, the "International Day of Human Space Flight". This celebration is held annually on 12th April to mark two special anniversaries in space exploration; the launch of Yuri Gagarin, the world's first space explorer, in 1961 and the first Space Shuttle *"Columbia"* launch in 1981.

The set of seven stamps all originated from the paintings of the six Apollo Moon landings by Al Bean. A further unique aspect of this issue was that five astronauts from these lunar missions agreed to sign 750 of the first-day covers. The covers included the appropriate stamp from the relevant mission and a filler card with details of each signatory. These included covers from moonwalkers, Alan Bean (Apollo 12), Edward Mitchell (Apollo 14) and Charles Duke (Apollo 15). The CMP's from Apollo's 12 and 15, Richard Gordon and Al Worden, also signed appropriate covers.

In 2012 the Isle of Man had seven locations on the Island designated as Dark Sky Discovery Sites (see chapter 6). This was followed in January 2014 by a further nineteen sites giving the Isle of Man the highest concentration of Dark Sky sites in the British Isles. It was suggested that a set of stamps to commemorate this achievement would be appropriate.

Following discussions, four stamps were produced and issued in September 2014. Each stamp featured a foreground night-time image from

IOM Post First Day cover signed by Apollo 12's moonwalker Alan Bean.

the Island and one of the principal seasonal constellations visible from the Island. The 42 pence stamp featured the winter constellation of Orion, as seen from Nairbyl. The £1.64 stamp featured the spring constellation of Leo from Port Erin. The £1.82 stamp featured the summer constellation of Cygnus from Fort Island, and the £2.30 stamp featured the autumn constellation of Pegasus from Langness. All four stamps also featured "Raad Mooar Ree Gorree" (the Milky Way), clearly seen from the Island's dark skies.

On the 20th March 2015, a total solar eclipse was visible from Scotland's north-western coast. This was seen as a partial eclipse from the Isle of Man, with the Sun being 92.8% eclipsed. At 9:32 AM, we saw just a thin sliver of sunlight below the Moon's limb covering the Sun. Many people recall the eclipse from 1999, which was total in Cornwall, and the Sun was 88.2% eclipsed, as seen from the IOM. Hence, the 2015 one was more spectacular for Isle of Man viewers. This eclipse was total in the northern Atlantic

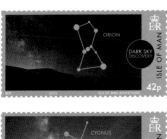

IOM Post Dark Sky Discovery stamps.

Ocean. Residents and visitors of the Faroe Isles saw totality for just under three minutes.

To commemorate this spectacular event, it was decided to produce another special issue using the Dark Skies stamps from the previous year on some commemorative covers. The issue was further enhanced by moonwalker Al Bean again agreeing to sign a limited number of the covers. Once again, I wrote the filler card, which featured eclipses seen from the Island since 1185. (See Eclipses chapter 9). IOM Post also produced a special collectable pack which included a signed envelope from Al Bean and postcards from the Faroe Islands.

In January 2016, the Isle of Man Post Office collaborated with the Royal Aeronautical Society (RAeS). It produced a set of stamps to celebrate 150 years since the RAeS's establishment in 1866. This set entitled "Innovation in Aerospace" featured eight stamps marking milestones in aviation, including three space exploration stamps. The launch of Sputnik in 1957, the launch of the first man in space Yuri Gagarin in 1961, and the establishment of the International Space Station. In December 2015, Major Tim Peake launched to the International Space Station and became the UK's first official astronaut. The first UK citizen to go into space was actually Helen Sharman back in 1991, but she flew as a private citizen. Tim, an ESA astronaut, launched on 15th December 2015 from the same Baikonur Cosmodrome in Kazakhstan, from where Yuri Gagarin launched on 12th April 1961. Tim returned to the Earth on 18th June 2016.

Through connections with the Royal Aeronautical Society, Tim took some of the Islands "Innovation in Aerospace" covers and signed a number of them for IOM Post.

Continuing with the scientific theme, later in 2016, a set of stamps

ESA Astronaut Tim Peake signing IOM stamps in the ISS Cupola. *(IOM Post)*

commemorating 100 years since the publication of Professor Albert Einstein's General Theory of Relativity was issued. It also celebrated the work of theoretical physicist Professor Stephen Hawking. The first two stamps show Albert Einstein and Stephen Hawking and their equations, $E = mc^2$ and $S = \frac{1}{4}A$, respectively. The third stamp illustrates the collision of two black holes, which gave rise to the discovery of gravitational waves in 2016, a phenomenon predicted by Einstein in the early twentieth century. The fourth stamp shows "Hawking Radiation", which Hawking showed could be emitted from black holes. The final two stamps show other depictions of black holes.

In 2018 to mark the anniversary of the film "*2001, a Space Odyssey*," a new issue was devised to commemorate this iconic film directed by renowned film director Stanley Kubrick. Stanley's daughter Katharina was invited to the Island to attend a special screening of the film. On behalf of IOM Post, I took Katharina and her partner on a tour of the Island, and she kindly signed my prized envelope.

Celebrating 50 years since the first lunar landing brought about two special commemorative issues. The first of these, "One Small step, 50 years of Lunar Exploration", was issued in April 2019. The stamps featured Project Apollo through to the second lunar landing of Apollo 12. The issue was endorsed by George Abbey, the former Director of the Johnson Space Flight Center.

The second set in the theme "One Giant leap – Exploring the Moon and Space" was issued in February 2020 and featured Apollo 13 through to Skylab, the Space Shuttle and the International Space Station. Retired NASA astronaut Charlie Duke signed some first day covers, as did Jay Honeycutt, former Director of the Kennedy Space Center.

The author with
Katharina Kubrick.

IOM Post "One Small Step" and "One Giant Leap" stamps issues.

Buzz Aldrin admires the "One small step" issue. *(IOM Post)*

Chapter 6

The Darker Skies of Mann

In recent years many people have become more aware of their natural environment. As we learn more and more about the amazing universe *(Yn tuinney)* in which we live, there has become an increasing awareness of the outstanding beauty of the splendours of the night skies. This increase in awareness of the environment in which we live is often attributed to the evocative and poignant images from the Apollo era, in particular, the famous "Earthrise" photograph taken from Apollo 8 as it orbited the Moon in December 1968.

Earthrise from Apollo 8 – December 1968. *(NASA)*

In the Isle of Man, this environmental awareness embraces our beautiful landscape and maritime environment, now acknowledged internationally as a UNESCO Biosphere Reserve, which also includes the wonders of our stunning Manx night skies. Since 2012 it has been formally recognised that the Isle of Man has some of the darkest night skies in the British Isles and Europe.

Since 1752 in the USA, when Benjamin Franklin deliberately flew his kite in a thunderstorm and consequently received an electrical shock, electricity has had a significant role in establishing and developing our human existence. In 1879 Thomas Edison, building on the work of others, patented what we call the incandescent light bulb. The first "switch on" of public electrical street lighting on Earth took place on 31st March 1880, in Wabash, Indiana, USA.

Just 13 years later, in the Isle of Man, on 7th September 1893, the Douglas and Laxey Coast Electric Tramway (DLCET) opened for business from the north end of Douglas Promenade to Groudle and carried over 20,000 passengers in just a few weeks until the line closed for the season. A few years later, the same Company installed the first-ever street lighting in the Isle of Man in Port Jack, Onchan. It is interesting to note that Douglas was, in fact, in 1923, one of the last towns of its size in the British Isles to install public electrical street lighting. This was despite the fact that the DLCET had provided such lighting in Port Jack over 20 years earlier. Lighting has since evolved from the first power-hungry incandescent bulbs to today's fluorescent and low power LED lights.

Whilst efficient lighting is an essential part of our human existence, it does not come without its problems. Excessive and inappropriate lighting has a negative side. Too much light affects our ability to see the stars in the night sky. "Light pollution" is now becoming a problem, not just for astronomers but for many aspects of the natural environment. There is evidence that excessive lighting affects the human circadian rhythm, the budding of trees, the insect life cycle, and bird migration. Lighting generation also is a significant contributor to the emission of "greenhouse" gases. On the adjacent Isles, the problems of light pollution and excessive lighting are effectively threatening the ability to see the splendours of the night sky. As a result, the night skies are, especially in urban areas, becoming a declining resource, threatened by development and the effects of intrusive artificial lighting.

The Isle of Man has been recognised as having very dark night skies for some time, a valued attribute of the rural character and tranquillity of the Island. Throughout history, numerous instances of significant astronomical observations have been undertaken on the Island, from the Cistercian Monks at Rushen Abbey, Bishop Wilson, and since the late nineteenth century, various astronomical societies.

The clarity of the sky has been recognised by the Isle of Man Government as important, not just for astronomers but also for future generations, who otherwise could grow up without ever seeing the beautiful sights in our dark night skies. The almost totally light pollution-free Manx skies mean that the sky can be quite spectacular on clear cloudless nights. Many astronomical sights can be seen with the naked eye. Even more can be discovered through a pair of binoculars or a telescope. Visitors to any part of the Island with dark skies *(Speyryn dorraghey)* can, unlike many on the neighbouring islands, see our galaxy, "Raad Mooar Ree Gorree," (The Milky Way). This shows up as a wispy cloud, estimated to be made up of around 500 billion stars. I should clarify that the number one billion refers to one thousand million. In 1974 the UK adopted this definition, having previously used one million million as a billion.

The Island is also ideal for seeing the magnificent sight of the Northern Lights. These are usually only seen from northern locations such as Alaska, Norway, Iceland and Northern Scotland. However, a clear northern horizon from the Island's north-western coast means this fascinating phenomenon can, on occasion, be seen from the Island.

In 2009, the UK Campaign for Dark Skies analysed the best places in the British Isles for stargazing, factoring in light pollution and cloud cover. Consequently, the UK Dark Skies Discovery network (DSDN) was established. Applications were invited for suitable sites throughout the British Isles to apply for listing. Dark Sky Discovery status is granted for areas that are fully accessible by the public, have good sightlines, and are suitable for persons of limited mobility. Cloud cover and inclement weather is always an issue for astronomers throughout the British Isles and northern Europe. However, on clear nights the clarity of the sky and the almost total lack of light pollution make the Isle of Man almost unique and a significant attraction for stargazing residents and British and international astronomers.

Later that year, our Manx astronaut Nicole Stott undertook a three-month stay on the ISS. Nicole observed the Island from space on several occasions. She remarked that she found it difficult to spot at night from her vantage point in orbit 400 km (250 miles) above the Earth. This was because so few lights were showing within its boundaries.

Nicole's observations of the Island helped us appreciate that the Island is not just a place with outstanding natural beauty but also has excellent night skies. Furthermore, unlike the adjacent Islands, the Isle of Man has very little in the way of light pollution. Consequently, the Island is justifiably considered one of the best places in the British Isles for stargazing.

In 2012, the Isle of Man Government's Department of Economic Development (DED) identified dark skies tourism as a potential niche market as part of its marketing strategy. In my role at MNH and as the chairman of the IOM Astronomical Society, I contacted the DSDN. They

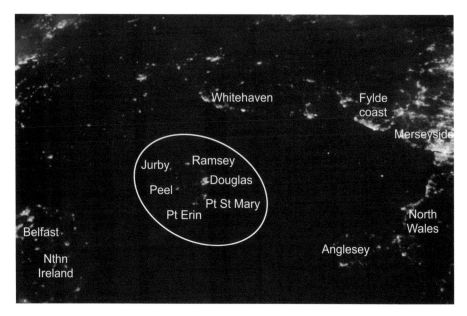

Whitehaven

Fylde
coast

Merseyside

Jurby · Ramsey

Peel · Douglas

Pt St Mary

Pt Erin

North
Wales

Belfast

Nthn
Ireland

Anglesey

The IOM from the
ISS, 12th September
2009. *(NASA)*

agreed that although the IOM is not part of the UK, they would include us in the network. Consequently, in May 2012, we invited Alan Brown, the North West coordinator of the DSDN, to the Island. Alan and I undertook a tour of the Island, and we identified twelve potential sites.

After some discussion, an application for seven of these was submitted to the DSDN in August 2012. As part of this application, The DED commissioned a short time-lapse film that highlighted the seven sites.

The seven sites for which the 2012 application was made comprised:

- In the east: Axnfell Plantation and Port Soderick Brooghs
- In the north: Smeale, and the Sulby reservoir car park
- In the west: Niarbyl
- In the South: The Sound and Fort Island

The application was supported by many local individuals and organisations, including astronaut Nicole Stott who had previously enthused about our dark and clear skies. In support of the application, Nicole stated…

"I tried on many occasions to identify the Isle of Man from orbit, but I had great difficulty because it is so dark! I eventually captured an image, and it shows how wonderful the night skies in the Island are. The Manx skies are fantastic for astronomy – great from above, on board the ISS and below, on the Island".

In October 2012, the DSDN in Edinburgh announced that all seven had been granted this prestigious status. This meant that the Isle of Man had a higher concentration of dark sky (*Speyryn gorraghey*) sites than any other area in the British Isles. The DSDN have two classifications of dark sky sites. Grade 1 sites are classified as those where just the principal stars of Orion are visible. Grade 2 sites are locations from where the Milky Way can be seen. All seven Manx sites were identified as Grade 2 sites, the highest standard awarded by the DSDN.

From an astronomical perspective, you can easily see the Milky Way on dark, clear moonless nights from all of these sites. All seven of the Isle of Man's sites scored up to 21.5 on a Sky Quality Meter (SQM), an instrument an astronomer uses to measure the darkness of a location. The scale goes from 16 (a light-polluted sky) to 22 (minimal or no pollution). A sky recording a value of 21 is more than 60 times darker than a city on the adjacent Isles.

Following this success, it was suggested that the IOM identify and establish some additional dark sky sites. Following discussions with the Government's "Visit Isle of Man" team, a public consultation was launched. As a consequence, an additional number of sites were identified, and following a detailed review in September 2013, 19 additional sites were submitted for DSDN approval.

The nineteen sites are:

- In the east: Conrhenny lower car park, The Clypse, Baldwin and Injebreck reservoirs, Port Soderick upper car park, Ballanette nature Reserve, Onchan Park, and the Mount Murray Golf club car park.
- In the north: Ballure reservoir, Glen Mooar beach, Mooragh Promenade.
- In the west: Ballaugh and Glen Wyllin beaches, the back of Peel Castle, Tynwald Mills car park.
- In the South: The Sloc, Cregneash, Rushen Abbey, and Poulsom Park.

Laxey Wheel, as shown on page 75, in a steep-sided valley, was not proposed as the Wheel area does not provide good sightlines of the sky, an essential requirement for a DSDN site.

With its illuminated golf driving range, Mount Murray Golf Club was initially dismissed. But following discussions with the club owners, it was agreed that the lights would be extinguished at 10.00 PM. Consequently, the site was included. In January 2014, all 19 were granted DSDN status. Meaning that the Isle of Man has the largest number of DSDN sites in the British Isles.

Since then, there have been numerous initiatives through the Visit Isle of Man programme. Signage has been erected at many of the 26 sites advising visitors what may be visible from these specific locations throughout the year. The "Stargazer friendly" package encourages

The Sound and Fort Island Dark Sky Discovery sites. *(Glen Whorrall)*

The Peel Castle Dark Sky Discovery Site. *(Glen Whorrall)*

The Cregneash Dark Sky Discovery Site. *(Ron Strathdee)*

Despite this spectacular image, Laxey Wheel
is NOT a Dark Sky Discovery Site. *(Sue Jones)*

The Sulby Reservoir car park (above) and Nairbyl (below) Dark Sky Discovery sites. *(Glen Whorrall)*

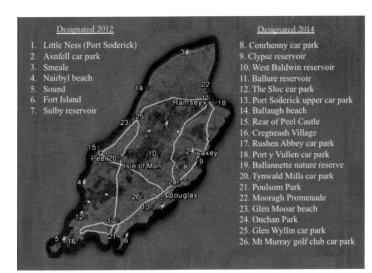

Designated 2012

1. Little Ness (Port Soderick)
2. Axnfell car park
3. Smeale
4. Nairbyl beach
5. Sound
6. Fort Island
7. Sulby reservoir

Designated 2014

8. Conrhenny car park
9. Clypse reservoir
10. West Baldwin reservoir
11. Ballure reservoir
12. The Sloc car park
13. Port Soderick upper car park
14. Ballaugh beach
15. Rear of Peel Castle
16. Cregneash Village
17. Rushen Abbey car park
18. Port y Vullen car park
19. Ballannette nature reserve
20. Tynwald Mills car park
21. Poulsom Park
22. Mooragh Promenade
23. Glen Mooar beach
24. Onchan Park
25. Glen Wyllin car park
26. Mt Murray golf club car park

IOM Dark Sky Discovery sites.

accommodation providers to include the Islands DSDN status, and the Visit Isle of Man blog (https://www.visitisleofman.com) features dark sky imagery and text.

Other organisations, including Event Services IOM, actively promote the Island's dark skies. The opportunity also exists for the Island to register with the International Dark Skies Association (IDA) organisation, possibly becoming the world's first dark skies nation. Alternatively, the Island could link up with UNESCO Biosphere status under their Starlight Initiative.

Little Ness Dark Sky signage.

Visit Isle of Man

Close to home but a welcome escape, the Isle of Man is waiting to welcome you with its open spaces, scenic landscapes and extraordinary dark skies.

Located in the heart of the Irish Sea, the Isle of Man is just a short flight or ferry trip from the UK, and truly offers something for everyone. With swathes of picture-perfect scenery, a dynamic food scene and rich history, the Island is geared up to steal your heart.

With its magnificent wildlife, beautiful hidden beaches and untouched flora and fauna, it's no wonder the Isle of Man is so renowned for its natural beauty. In fact, the entire Island has UNESCO Biosphere status – the first nation in the world to have achieved this. Its diverse landscape offers a unique getaway that encompasses all you'll need for a break from everyday life. Rolling glens unfold into stunning beaches in the blink of an eye, and whether you're looking for a hiking getaway in the great outdoors or to enjoy clear, starry skies in one of the Island's 26 accredited Dark Sky Discovery Sites, the Island's beauty provides the perfect retreat from life's daily distractions.

For an Island so small, 13 miles wide by 33 miles long to be exact, it sure has it all. Culture and castles, landmarks and landscapes, rolling hills and botanical gardens; it's an Island shrouded in folklore, myth and heritage. Step back in time and piece together the history of the British Isles' best-kept secret. Follow the footsteps of Norse Kings in the hallways of Castle Rushen, unearth fascinating history at Viking burial sites or immerse yourself in the Island's many museums. Take the electric railway and explore the east coast, or hop on the historical steam railway for a nostalgic trip through the heart of the Isle of Man.

Once your heart's full of nature and culture, why not stop to fill up on something a little more culinary? The Isle of Man offers some of the finest food experiences in the British Isles as its wild, rugged landscape lends itself beautifully to home-grown creations. From beach cafes to fine dining restaurants, food stalls to farm shops, you're never far from a thriving foodie scene that promises to deliver on taste each and every time.

Sometimes getting out of the city is all you need to recharge and rejuvenate, and with 40% of the Isle of Man uninhabited, there's plenty of space to live the rural dream. From wildest coast to deepest countryside, the Island has a real mix of basic and luxury accommodation to suit all tastes and budgets, and given the Island's compact size, you're never too far from the hustle and bustle when you want to catch a break from solitude.

Uncover more at
visitisleofman.com

 /VISITISLEOFMAN

 INSTAGRAM.COM/VISITISLEOFMAN

 YOUTUBE.COM/VISITISLEOFMAN

 @VISITISLEOFMAN

Chapter 7

Meteoroids, Meteors, Meteorites and Comets

There is a popular misconception that the night sky is static and unchanging ever since our forefathers first looked up at it. However, in reality, nothing could be further from the truth. The stars rise four minutes earlier each day, which gives us a daily and seasonal variation. In addition, the Sun, Moon and planets all have a distinct and predictable motion across the sky. We can also observe eclipses and various atmospheric features such as aurorae and noctilucent clouds. Then we have a class of objects seen in the night sky, which are in a category of their own: meteoroids, meteors, meteorites and comets.

All four of these can be placed in the category of "Visitors from Space", but I tend not to use that title in my talks and lectures as people often think I will talk about extra-terrestrial life, which is another subject altogether.

Meteoroids: are small particles that are found in space. Like most other objects in our solar system, they orbit the Sun (or other stars) and vary in size from small dust grains to a few metres in diameter. When a meteoroid collides with a planet's atmosphere, it becomes a meteor.

Meteors: are meteoroids that impact upon the upper atmosphere of a body and usually burn up upon entry into the atmosphere producing a visible light trace or "shooting star" effect as they descend through the atmosphere. On occasion, meteors may "bounce off" the atmosphere and return to being meteoroids. Such objects are usually no larger than a pebble or a grain of sand. They impact the upper atmosphere at very high speeds. Their kinetic energy is converted to light and thus seen as a meteor that may have a trail. Most meteors in the Earth's atmosphere first appear at a height of 140 km (85 miles).

Meteorites: are meteors that survive their passage through the atmosphere and reach the ground or sea level. We have also observed meteoric impacts on the Moon and meteorites on Mars.

Comets: best described as "dirty snowballs" by US astronomer Frank Whipple in 1950, comprise frozen gases, rock and dust that orbit the Sun in eccentric orbits. The central part of a comet is its "nucleus". This is usually about 16 km (10 miles) wide. As it approaches "perihelion" (closest approach to the Sun), parts of the nucleus can melt. It will then form a "coma", which can be as large as 75,000 km (46,600 miles) wide and create a "tail", which can be over 10 million km (6.2 million miles) long.

Meteoroids

There are three significant types of meteoroids.
1. When the solar system was formed approximately 4.5 billion years ago, a considerable amount of material was leftover. Much of this material was then "collected" gravitationally by larger objects such as planets, moons and asteroids.
2. When a comet is before, at or after perihelion, material can melt and come away from the nucleus and stream out behind it. This material forms a tail. Over many years, this material spreads out as meteoroids. It orbits the Sun in the same way as the comet itself. If the Earth intercepts these meteoroids on its annual passage around the Sun, such material may then impact the Earth's atmosphere and may be seen as meteors.
3. The third type of meteoroid originates from other celestial bodies such as the Moon, Mars and asteroids. Following impact events, some material may be ejected into space. This material can become meteoroids which can then possibly impact upon the Earth's upper atmosphere.

Meteors

Meteors can be described in many ways, including:
1. A "falling" or "shooting star" names for meteors seen as they brighten or burn up as they enter the atmosphere. Ancient observers believed that this was a star falling from its fixed position. Hence the name "falling" or "shooting star".
2. "Fireballs" are brighter meteors that may also leave a trail of sparks
3. "Bolides" are much larger meteors that are very bright, usually because they explode in the atmosphere as they enter and descend. An unofficial definition of a bolide is a fireball that is brighter than the Full Moon *(lane easyt)*.

Meteors tend to be very fast and typically enter the atmosphere at 10 to 30 km per second (6 to 18 miles per second) or 30 times faster than a bullet.

There are also two distinct types of meteors seen in our skies:
1. "Sporadic meteors," or "sporadic's", are random meteors that can appear anywhere in the sky. They are not predictable, and they can vary in size and brightness. Meteors can also be caused by spacecraft debris burning up in our atmosphere. Some re-entering larger spacecraft can be tracked as they disintegrate and recorded. Examples of this were Skylab, the NASA space laboratory in 1979, and the Russian' Mir space station in 2001.

2. "Meteor showers" are seen when the Earth intercepts material streaming out along a comet's orbit. The comet may have disappeared in some cases, but the material may still be present, and we may see a meteor shower at the same time each year.

All major meteor showers have a parent body from which the shower originates. This is known as the "progenitor". In most cases, this is from a comet, but a few showers also originate from asteroids. Most showers tend to have distinct peaks over a period of years. This occurs because as the parent comet nears the Sun, it may undergo significant outgassing and brighten considerably. When this happens, it sheds a significant amount of material that may spread out in clumps behind the comet. If the Earth, on its orbit, intercepts such a clump of material, then a shower or possibly a "meteor storm" may occur. An example of this is the Leonids which tend to have dramatic peaks every 33 years. The next potential "storm" could occur in 2031.

Because of the geometry of the solar system, the Earth's orbit may intercept a comet's path twice a year. When this happens, two showers may be seen with the same progenitor at different times of the year. An example of this is the Eta Aquarids in May and the Orionids in October. Both have Comet Halley as their progenitor. All meteors from showers radiate from the same distinct point in the night sky, called the "radiant". The shower is named after the constellation that the radiant point is in. Meteors from a shower can appear anywhere in the sky. If you trace the path of any meteor back to a known radiant within a constellation, then it will bear its name. For example, the Leonids, Perseids and Geminid showers radiate from their specific constellations. If you trace a meteor back to a different location, then it is a sporadic meteor. There have been dozens of meteor showers identified, varying in intensity and duration.

Observing meteors

There is something fascinating about watching material, either debris from the solar system's birth or from other celestial bodies appearing as meteors in our night skies. It is always worth looking out for them, especially at the time of the major meteor showers. I can suggest a few essential tips to see some meteors for yourself. However, I do have a somewhat ruthless meteor spotting rule. Unless two or more people see one, it does not count!

Where to go to watch a meteor shower: Whilst you can comfortably watch meteors from many places, your own back garden is ideal if there is little in the way of light pollution. Rural areas are good but do ensure they have a wide-open viewing area with little light pollution. For this reason, roadside car parks are not usually suitable because of encroaching vehicle

Leonids – November 1966.

lights. Most meteor showers tend to radiate from constellations rising in the eastern sky. I tend to use south-easterly facing dark sky sites. Most of the Islands dark sky sites, by definition, are ideal with good horizon views. Any view out to sea will be good as light pollution will be minimal.

Minimal Moonlight: On a clear night, the best time to look for meteors is when we have no bright moonlight in the night sky. Moonlight can be a problem, particularly if a Full Moon occurs on or around the dates of a shower's peak. However, it will still be worth going out to look as meteors can appear anywhere in the sky. If the Moon is in the east, then the northern, western and southern horizons will be worth looking towards. Most meteors from showers tend to be more numerous in constellations adjacent to the radiant constellation. Although most meteor shower radiants

Perseids over the Calf of Man – August 2018. *(Ron Strathdee)*

rise from the eastern horizon, this is usually the best direction to look. There are, however, two northern meteor showers, the Quadrantids and the Ursids. Consequently, these tend to be seen when you face the northern horizon.

Dates: Meteors from most showers can usually be seen a few days before and after the peak. The actual peak can be quite specific and produce a prolific display over a short sharp period. This is caused by the Earth intercepting the debris stream as it orbits the Sun. The actual time of the peak does vary on an annual basis, but the dates tend to be quite specific. So, be aware of the dates of the showers and also look a few days before and after the anticipated peak.

Timing: When you are in a vehicle during a rainy spell, take a look at the windows. Which windows get the most rain? It will always be the one facing the direction of travel. The same applies to meteors. As the Earth turns on its axis, you will be facing travel direction after midnight. So, we tend to see more meteors in the sky after midnight. This also increases the likelihood of us observing meteor trails.

Most important:

1. **A dark sky:** The main thing you need to become a proficient meteor spotter is a dark sky. It's possible to see a bright meteor or two or even more from well-lit urban areas, but if you want to see several meteors a minute, including fainter meteors and their trails, avoid well-lit areas.
2. **Comfort:** A reclining chair such as a sun lounger, a blanket, and a thermos of something hot will make the meteor observing session very comfortable.

Another issue is the date of the shower. We get considerably fewer hours of darkness from our Manx latitude of 54.2 degrees north in the summer months. Although meteors can occur at any time of the day, we can only see those that happen in a dark sky. Some astronomers can detect daytime meteors by radar, but this is quite a specialist field.

The Zenith hourly rate (ZHR)

This is a term used by astronomers to indicate how many meteors you can hope to see in an hour. The "zenith" is the term used to describe the point in the sky directly above an observer. If a meteor shower's radiant coincides with an observer's zenith at the same time as the shower's peak, then meteors will radiate from this point in every direction, so, with half of the celestial globe above your horizon, you may see the maximum number of meteors. The ZHR is the number of meteors you can expect to see if the zenith is overhead and the peak occurs at this time. In reality, most radiant's tend to rise in the east, so we would expect to see only half of the anticipated number if the radiant point is on the horizon. However, do not be put off. Even if the radiant is below your horizon, meteors may still stream from that source into the sky visible above your horizon.

In summary, the best time to see meteors is on a date within the date range, on a clear, moonless night after midnight. (See Table 1 below). But meteor spotting can be frustrating. If you see one and try and tell your companion(s), but unless they are looking at the same part of the sky, the chances are they won't see it. On many occasions, I have been meteor spotting with a group, and I will be facing them whilst they are looking at the sky behind me. Someone will say, "*Wow! did you see that meteor*". Many of the group will have seen it, but it will be gone when I turn around and look in that direction.

Meteorites

By definition, a meteor that survives its passage through the Earth's atmosphere and can be ultimately found and identified is called a meteorite. To survive such an atmospheric passage and make landfall, they have to have been quite large in size at the point of entry into our atmosphere. Scientists worldwide search diligently to find them. They analyse their content and ascertain their age and origins. Most meteorites tend to be dark in colour, and so the best place to find meteorites are places where the landscape is light by contrast. Hence, deserts and ice-covered areas tend to be where most meteorites are found.

Due to the intense heat and pressure that such objects endure on their

Table 1: The major meteor showers visible from the Isle of Man

Name	Peak date	Date range	Dec.*	Speed	ZHR	Progenitor (Parent)
Quadrantids	03-Jan	28/12-12/1	49	Med	110	Asteroid 03EH1
Lyrids	22-Apr	14-30/4	34	Med	18	C.Thatcher
Eta Aquariids	05-May	19-28/5	-1	Fast	50	C.Halley
Perseids	12-Aug	17/7-24/8	58	Fast	100	C.Swift-Tuttle
Draconids	08-Oct	6-20/10	54	Slow	10	C.Giacobini-Zimmer
Taurids (S)	10-Oct	10/9-20/11	9	Slow	5	C.Encke
Orionids	21-Oct	2/10-7/11	16	Fast	20	C.Halley
Taurids (N)	12-Nov	20/10-10/12	22	Slow	5	Asteroid 04TG10
Leonids	17-Nov	6-30/11	22	V/fast	10	C.Tempel-Tuttle
Geminids	14-Dec	4-20/12	33	Slow	150	Asteroid Phaeton
Ursids	22-Dec	17-26/12	76	Slow	10	C.Tuttle
* Dec. = Declination, the height of the radiant above the celestial equator						

passage through the atmosphere, they can often explode and be seen as fireballs or bolides. Such an event occurred on 15th February 2014. A large meteor, estimated to be approximately 17 metres (56 feet) in diameter with a mass of about 10,000 tonnes, exploded about 25 km (16 miles) above the Russian town of Chelyabinsk. There were over 1,000 injuries caused mainly by broken glass. A large meteorite from this event created a hole in a frozen lake and was later recovered.

A sobering thought is that the latitude of Chelyabinsk is 55.1 degrees north. This compares to the Point of Ayre in the north of the Isle of Man at 54.4 degrees north. If the impact had occurred just a few hours later, the northern Irish Sea would have been in the firing line, and we could possibly have seen it. Coincidently Lockerbie in Scotland is precisely at the same latitude.

There is considerable evidence that meteoric impacts on Earth have had a significant effect on life on our planet. One credible theory is that during the "early bombardment" period, about 4 billion years ago, the inner terrestrial planets in the solar system were bombarded by asteroids, comets and meteors. It is postulated that the ice in comets brought to the Earth gave

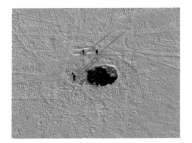

The meteorite which punched a hole in this lake *(left, image Eduard Kalinin)* was recovered *(right, image Anton Melnikov/Reuters)* and displayed at the local museum.

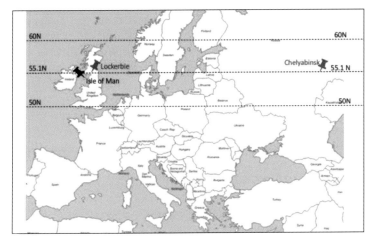

Chelyabinsk and the IOM – Latitude.

us our water during this period. Some scientists think that it is this which led to life evolving on Earth.

There is clear evidence of such impacts throughout history. The Moon, with no atmosphere to protect it, shows clear signs of prolific meteoric impact over the millennia, and impacts have also been recorded in recent years. Many Earth impacts have also been discovered by satellite imagery and geophysical data. The best known of these is the Barringer Crater in Arizona, USA. This impact which 50,000 years ago, was caused by a meteorite estimated to be 80 to 100 metres (260 to 330 feet) in diameter, leaving a crater over 1.3 km (0.8 miles) in diameter and 174 metres (570 feet) deep.

This is, however, not the largest crater found on Earth. That distinction belongs to the Vredefort Crater, a 300 km (190 miles) crater in South Africa. The main crater has mostly eroded, but its size can be deduced from the remnants of the central features of the dome. It is estimated that the meteorite that caused this feature was about 15 km (9 miles) in diameter. There is also overwhelming evidence that a similarly sized object caused a "mass extinction" event responsible for the dinosaurs' demise. The Chicxulub Crater, under the Yucatan Peninsula in Mexico, is thought to have been the location for such an event. Parts of the crater ring is still visible, and the crater is estimated to be about 150 km (90 miles in diameter. The impact occurred 66 million years ago. This date coincided with the Cretaceous-Tertiary (K-T) extinction event when over 75% of plant and animal life on Earth became extinct. In 1980, Luis and Walter Alvarez suggested that the Chicxulub impact caused this K-T extinction event. This theory is supported by the discovery of a layer of Iridium, a comparatively rare element on Earth but found in meteorites, which has been identified at the Cretaceous/Tertiary geological boundary.

If you run a magnet along the inside of the gutters of your home you may discover small black fragments that are iron- rich debris from micro-meteorites. I have looked without success for evidence of any Manx meteorites without success, depite rumours of a one being displayed at the old Derby Castle in Douglas. A few years ago a bright fireball appeared in Manx skies, and several Manx astronomers went looking for a meteorite that may have landed on the Island. Eventually, a fragment from this fireball was found in Northumberland. In February 2021, a meteor was seen across the skies of central England, and the following day meteorite fragments were found on a driveway in Winchcombe, Gloucester. The largest UK find for over 30 years.

Comets *(Comaid)*

Unlike meteors or shooting stars, which appear to "shoot" rapidly across the sky, comets appear to be slow-moving and are seen in the same part of the sky for days or weeks. They are, however, moving rapidly, at speeds over 100,000 kmph (62,000 mph) when nearing the Sun at perihelion. All comets are in elliptical orbits of various sizes and return to the solar vicinity at intervals dictated by the size of the ellipse.

Comets, or "hairy stars" as they used to be described, are features of the night sky that are unpredictable. Today, unlike years ago, when comets could only be discovered with the unaided eye, comets can be detected using telescopes and spacecraft when they are far out in the solar system. Once detected, the orbit can be calculated, and we can work out when and where they may be visible. They are spectacular objects to observe, primarily because most develop magnificent tails. When a comet approaches perihelion, ices in the nucleus start to sublimate (turn directly from solid to gas). This material then forms the comet's coma. In a large comet, the coma can be substantial. The material in the coma will then be removed from the coma by the incoming solar wind and form a tail. This will then stream out behind the nucleus and coma and will always point away from the Sun. Most comets develop at least two different tails, a dust and an ion trail, which each adds to the visual beauty of a comet's appearance.

All comets are thought to originate in an area in the Solar system known as the "Oort Cloud", named after the Dutch astronomer Jan Oort, who discovered it in 1950. The Oort Cloud is believed to be a giant spherical shell surrounding the Sun and planets between 2,000 and 200,000 astronomical units (AU) from the Sun. The AU is the Earth's mean distance from the Sun, 150 million km (93 million miles). The Oort Cloud is considered to be an area where material dating back to the Solar system's origin resides. Occasionally two or more objects will pass close to each for their weak gravitational fields to interact. This may result in a change in their orbit. Many comets orbit just outside the orbit of the planets. But some may be gravitationally perturbed by one of the "gas giant planets" (Jupiter, Saturn, Uranus and Neptune). Such comets then head into the inner solar system and may be seen from the Earth. There is a theory that a passing star disturbs the Oort Cloud every 200 million years or so. This may cause mass extinction events, which have been recorded throughout the Earth's history.

Comets have been seen throughout history, and often such sightings brought fear and apprehension. Some ancient cultures saw comets as weapons of the Gods. Their unpredictability was seen as a message of displeasure and impending doom.

In 1705, Edmund Halley predicted that a comet seen in 1682 would return 76 years later in 1758. He never saw the return, having died in 1742, but it was given his name when the comet returned in 1758. Looking back at the sightings of Halley's comet throughout history, we now know that a comet in 240 BC and possibly as early as 467 BC was Comet Halley. We have records of the "perihelic passage" of Comet Halley on at least 31 occasions.

In 1066 a comet seen in England was thought to be an omen, and for King Harold, who was to die at Hastings, it was indeed a bad omen. However, for William the Conqueror, it was a good omen.

As a consequence of William's victory, the comet is shown on the Bayeux Tapestry. In 1066, Comet Halley came within 0.10 AU from the Earth. It was recorded as being a quarter of the Full Moon's brightness. So, it must have been quite dramatic in our skies all those years ago.

In 1986 the apparition was poor as the comet was still 0.59 AU from us at its closest to Earth. It was much brighter in 1910 when it was 0.15 AU distant. In 1986 the nucleus of Comet Halley was estimated to be about 10 x 15 km (6 x 9 miles) in diameter. The coma was estimated to have been 100,000 km (62,000 miles) in diameter. The tail was well over 50 million km (31 million miles) in length.

Comet Halley's next perihelion is in 2061, when it will be 0.48 AU away at its closest and will be even closer in 2134. On 2nd November 2023, Comet Halley's will be at its furthest distance from the Sun (aphelion) and start making its way back to the inner solar system.

There is little mention in the Manx newspapers of Comet Halley being seen in 1910. I did, however, find a reference to "the Comet" in Castletown Heritage's occasional papers. In this Charles Watterson, and William Clague reminisce about seeing the comet in April 1910. It was seen from Queen Street. Low in the sky, directly over Scarlett. It is described as magnificent with a shiny head and a multicoloured tail.

In 1986 sightings of the Comet were recorded extensively in the Manx

Halley's Comet 1986. *(ESA)*

media and many people on the Isle of Man recall seeing it. Many others saw the bright comets, Kohoutek in 1996 and Hale Bopp in 1997. These two Comets seen in the Manx skies helped raise public awareness and helped raise funds to build the IOMAS Observatory.

Back in 2007, another comet, Comet Holmes, approached perihelion. It was expected to be well below naked-eye visibility, but something (we believe it was major outgassing) caused the comet to brighten dramatically. It was easily visible as a naked-eye object in the constellation of Perseus. It was clearly observed in the Manx night sky. I recall seeing it one evening whilst in London, very easily seen despite light-polluted skies. Unfortunately, the tail was not visible when it was brightest as it was pointing directly away from us.

I have been fortunate to have seen several comets over the years. Comet NEOWISE (Near-Earth Object Wide-field Infrared Survey Explorer) was an unexpected treat in 2020, but it was only visible in the early morning sky in June.

Since the dawn of the space age, we have been exploring comets with spacecraft. In 1986 the ESA spacecraft "Giotto" intercepted Comet Halley

Hale-Bopp 1997.
(Jake Huxley)

Comet NEOWISE over Douglas Bay – June 2020. *(Kevin Deakes)*

Comet NEOWISE over Bradda Head – June 2020. *(Ron Strathdee)*

passing less than 600 km (375 miles) from the nucleus. Unfortunately, NASA's mission to Comet Halley was lost in the Challenger disaster. In recent years, the most dramatic success was the arrival and orbiting of Comet 67P/ Churyumov-Gerasimenko by the "Rosetta" spacecraft in 2014. This mission also deployed a small lander, "Philae". This "Manx" lander (well, it did have three legs!) failed to secure itself securely to the surface. Still, it did send back invaluable data about the surface conditions, which helped add to our understanding of comets and their role in our solar system.

Comets can also be in parabolic (or long-term orbits) or even hyperbolic orbits, when a comet can be slung out of the solar system, having received a gravitational slingshot from the Sun.

In 2017 an object was discovered, thought initially to be a comet passing through the Solar system from interstellar space. Astronomer Robert Weryk in Hawaii saw the object after its perihelic passage when it was about 33 million km (21 million miles) from Earth. It was named Oumuamua, Hawaiian for "*a messenger from afar arriving first*". It was estimated to be roughly 30 x 30 x 160 metres (100 by 100 by 500 feet) proportions similar to that of a fire extinguisher. The elongated shape made it somewhat unusual and untypical of other cometary objects. Despite its proximity to the Sun, it had no signs of a coma. Its trajectory indicated that it would leave the solar system, having sufficient velocity to escape the Sun's gravitation grasp. Despite media suggestions that it may have been of alien

Opposite: Comet NEOWISE from the Point of Ayre – June 2021. *(James Brew)*

origin, in 2019, scientists concluded that it was a natural object from outside the solar system.

This was followed by another object in 2019. Comet Borisov was also deduced to have come from outside the Solar system. Unlike Oumuamua, it developed a coma and tail. This is now described as the first-ever observed interstellar comet.

Comet Borisov was estimated to be travelling at 175,000 kmph. (109,000 mph). However, the fastest recorded comet was observed travelling at over 2.16 million kmph (1.34 million mph) before it was absorbed by the Sun.

Finally, on the subject of comets, I can advise there are officially exists a class of comets called "Manx comets", which are comets without tails. Manx comets are dark and virtually tailless. They are thought to be mainly comprised of rock, similar to the rocky asteroids located in the region between Mars and Jupiter. There is conjecture that planets, moons, and asteroids may have migrated from one location to another in the ancient past of our Solar system's evolution. Thus, objects such as our Manx comets may have moved away from their original site to the outer solar system.

The three-legged
Philae heads for
Comet 67P. *(ESA)*

Chapter 8

Observing the Northern Lights (aurora borealis/ *Lossan ny Twoaie*)

As an astronomer, I have been fortunate enough to have seen quite a few spectacular sights in the night sky, and some stand out. The two solar eclipses in Turkey in 2006 and the US in 2017, two transits of the planet Venus in 2004 and 2012 and the Perseid meteor shower in 2015 spring to mind. But another warrants a special mention because we can see it, albeit infrequently, from the Isle of Man. The popular and stunning phenomenon of the northern lights or aurora borealis can occasionally be seen from Manx shores. The word "aurora" is the Latin word for lights, and the word "borealis" means northern. Aurora "australis" can also be visible in the southern hemisphere, australis being Latin for southern.

The aurora (borealis and australis) are normally only seen from the world's polar regions, in the northern hemisphere, from inside the Arctic circle. Consequently, it can frequently be seen from locations such as Alaska, Norway and Iceland. However, a clear northern horizon from the Isle of Man's north-western coast means that the aurora borealis can, on occasion, be seen from the Island.

The aurora is one of these phenomena that many people, even with only a passing interest in astronomy, really want to see. Many organised trips, cruises, and flights are arranged to see this amazing natural phenomenon. To see it from your home location is quite special.

I saw another great auroral display from Niarbyl in April 2000. The IOMAS was holding a star party at the old Niarbyl café. About 25 of us attended that night. After a drink and a snack, being a clear night, we went outside to undertake some stargazing. It was not long before we realised that something special was happening at the northern horizon. As we stood, full of anticipation and some degree of excitement, we watched as an auroral display developed. We stayed until about 11.00 PM, and then on the way home, we had Manx Radio on in the car, and they were asking about what was happening in the Manx night sky that night. Once I got home, it was still visible from our home in Onchan, so I contacted Manx Radio and advised them of the display. We were to learn later that many Manx residents went out and were able to see what was quite a spectacular auroral display. The year 2000 display was the first of quite a few aurorae I have managed to see from Manx shores. We had another impressive display on 1st April 2004, which was certainly no April fool's day prank.

It is important to realise that an auroral display might not occur despite

Aurora over the IOMAS Observatory 2000. *(James Martin)*

all of the necessary conditions being met at the outset. For example, there may be an excellent display of stars at a dark location inside the Arctic circle on a clear night with no moonlight and quite likely a great view of the Milky Way, but no aurorae. I recall back in 2013 undertaking a stargazing session on a ship in Norway. It was a fantastic night for stargazing, but there was no aurorae whatsoever. It was such a shame, as so many people wanted to see some aurorae, so there were quite a few disappointed aurorae chasers despite my best efforts. We did, however, see some aurorae the following night.

The best aurorae I have ever seen was in 2014 when I was on a cruise ship in Norway. One night at about 8.30 PM, we were docked in Tromso, Norway, and Sandra and I were doing the trivia quiz in the lounge. Someone came in from outside as said, *"Aren't you the astronomy bloke? You should be outside"*. I went out, and despite the bright lights of the port and inadequate clothing, a spectacular auroral display was visible. We put our cold-weather clothing on and went up on deck. By this time, we had left Tromso, and Sandra and I joined many guests on deck. We had a fantastic night observing. I made a promise to myself to stay until everyone else had gone to bed and I finally left at about 3.00 AM. The display was still visible but was showing signs of diminishing. I also discovered that French hot chocolate (brandy and hot chocolate) is an excellent auroral drink. After two or three of them, the aurora is quite spectacular!

Opposite top: Aurora over St Marks 2004. *(Jake Huxley)*

Opposite bottom: Aurora from Tromso, Norway – March 2014.

There was an interesting sequel to this viewing. The following day, I delivered a lecture in the theatre. I started by asking if everyone had seen the previous night's display? The response was initially positive from about

90% of attendees, but there was a small but vociferous group on my right who had missed it totally and were grumbling that they had not seen anything. At this point, I ought to say that most aurorae cruises have a straightforward procedure. They will not announce a display over the public address system but suggest leaving your TV on a specific channel. They will update the situation as and when a display develops. So, if you do go on an aurorae cruise, remember this useful tip!

A similar thing happened again in 2019. I was onboard the Viking Sun, sailing from Norway to Canada via Iceland. I was on deck stargazing and I kept getting asked if we could see any aurorae. Despite it being a clear night there was no sign. However, I did spot a smear of white on the northern horizon but I was uncertain if it was aurorae, so I said nothing. Eventually, it did develop but by then there was only about 20 of us left on deck. It was not a spectacular display but it was the only aurorae we spotted on that trip.

In 1608 Hans Lippershey, a Dutch eyeglass maker, invented the first telescope. In 1610 Galileo Galilei used such an instrument for the first time for astronomy and made many significant discoveries. This included the first observations of sunspots *(Cron greiney)*. Galileo's observations of these "spots" on the solar disc contributed to him believing that the Sun was not a perfect unblemished object orbiting the Earth. It was, as Nicholas Copernicus had suggested in 1543, an object at the centre of our Solar system that the Earth orbited and not the other way around. Sunspots are areas on the Sun with a lower temperature than the surrounding area, so they appear darker. By projecting the Sun's image onto a card or screen it is possible to observe such sunspots. **You should never observe the Sun directly as it could cause serious damage or blindness.** Using this "projection" technique it is possible to record the number of sunspots on the solar disc. Using such observations, it becomes apparent that the Sun has a distinctive eleven-year cycle of activity. The peak and lower levels of this activity are called the "solar maxima" and "solar minima". The intensity of auroral displays tend to follow this cycle, with a peak at solar maxima.

There is much speculation as to why the Sun has such a distinctive cycle and the effects it has, not just on the aurorae but on the Earth in general. Aurorae have also been observed in the upper atmosphere of the planets Jupiter and Saturn. They are also thought to occur in the Venusian and Martian atmospheres.

Auroral displays are caused by the incoming "solar wind", the intensity of which is also affected by the solar maxima and minima. The solar wind is a stream of electrons and protons that can travel as fast as 750 km/second (450 mp/second). Our planet is surrounded by a magnetic field. When this incoming solar wind reaches the vicinity of the Earth three days later, some of the charged particles are attracted by the magnetic field to the upper atmosphere, near the polar regions. When these particles collide with atoms in the Earth's atmosphere, it releases energy in the form of light, which then causes the formation of colourful aurorae in the polar regions of the Earth's atmosphere.

The most common colour of the aurorae is green, caused by oxygen. Upper atmosphere oxygen can also produce red aurorae, whilst yellow, purple and blue aurorae are caused by nitrogen. Auroral displays usually take the form of an auroral oval centred on the Earth's magnetic poles. The size of the auroral oval will depend on the quantity of incoming material from the solar wind, which is itself dependent on the level of activity on the Sun. If the solar activity is at a higher level, then the auroral oval will extend southwards, and aurorae may be seen much further south than usual. One benefit from being so far south is that you may see the red aurorae, which tends to sit above the more common green coloured aurorae. In recent years a new type of aurorae has been observed. "Black Aurora". This is thought to be caused by the opposite of the traditional aurorae. Electrons are moving upwards rather than in typical auroral displays in which electrons move downwards.

On occasion, the Sun can erupt a vast amount of material in the form of a "coronal mass ejection"(CME). CME's are often associated with other forms of solar activity. There is still no firm conclusion about their origin, but it is thought that they usually originate from groupings of sunspots. However, there may be as many as three CME's per day near the period of solar maxima compared to just one every five days at solar minima. An individual CME may comprise over a billion tons of matter that can be

Aurora over Peel Castle, October 2015. *(James Brew)*

Aurora over Ballaugh
– Isle of Man,
October 2015.
(James Brew)

accelerated to a speed of several million km per hour. If it is directed to and reaches Earth, the shock wave of the travelling mass impacts the Earth's magnetosphere and usually, but not always, causes powerful auroral displays in large regions around Earth's polar regions. CME's can also disrupt communication and cause damage to satellites, electrical transmission systems and cause power cuts. In 2002 and 2012, major CME's were observed by spacecraft. These did not impact the Earth's atmosphere as we were at a different point in our orbit when the CME reached the Earth's orbital distance from the Sun. If the Earth had been at this location at this time, the effects could have been quite dramatic.

The last solar maxima was in 2014, and the current period reached minima in 2019. We are now starting to see a slight increase in activity as we head towards the next peak in 2024/25. The last few peaks have been significantly lower than previously, leading to a reduced level of aurorae being visible. However, there is some evidence that the next peak (cycle number 25) is possibly going to be a little higher than the previous cycle.

Predicting Aurorae

Whilst aurorae can be very elusive and variable in intensity, they are not totally unpredictable. These days with a profusion of solar observatories and satellites, we are beginning to understand more and more about the workings of our nearest star. There are now several online auroral prediction sites with a relatively high degree of success.

There are three principal ways to predict auroral displays:

- Using the "Kp-index"
- The location of the "auroral ovation".
- Analysis of the solar rotation

The most commonly used method uses the "planetary K index" or the "Kp-index". This is primarily used for daily or short-term predictions. It is a scale that measures the geomagnetic activity in the polar regions, which, if high, can lead to an auroral display. The Kp-index goes from one to nine. The higher the Kp-index, the greater the intensity of the display and the further south you will possibly see an auroral display. A Kp-index of five or above is typically required to see aurorae from the Isle of Man or from a latitude of about 50 degrees north of the equator. However, the Kp-index does take a little time to be updated, and an intense display may come and go before the index can be updated.

- Kp 1 to 3: Aurorae are usually quiet and faint. The predominant colour is green, and aurorae are not likely to be seen from the latitude of the IOM.
- Kp 4 to 6: There is an increased amount of auroral activity. They will possibly show vivid colours like yellow, bluish, or purple tones in the polar regions. Aurorae may be visible on the northern horizon from Manx shores and at lower latitudes, such as northern England or the northern states of the USA.
- Kp 7 to 9: The aurorae are very active. They can cover the entire sky from the polar regions and show rarer colours like red. We may see the auroral coronas high in the sky, and aurorae may be seen from the southern UK and elsewhere.

Once an aurora gets to Kp level 5, it is classed as storm grade G1, and storm grades can rise to storm grade G5 (Kp 9), which is the maximum. However, a word of caution, the Kp-index is not 100% accurate, but it is undoubtedly one of the best forecast indicators. So, you might just see a strong display with a low Kp-index. Conversely, a high Kp-index may lead to no visible aurorae.

The "Auroral Ovation forecast" is another short-term auroral forecast method. We know that aurorae occur in an oval centred on the Earth's magnetic poles. This will be overhead in places like Norway, Alaska and Canada. From locations further south, aurorae may be seen on the northern horizon. As the intensity of a display increases, the oval increases in size, so aurorae may be seen further south. To see a display from latitude 54 degrees north (or south), you need to be within 500 miles from the southern edge of the oval.

The only regularly used long-term auroral forecast method is by using solar rotation. The Sun rotates on its axis once every 27 days. Therefore, if we see a display, it may also be seen approximately four weeks later.

There are now several aurora "apps" which can provide forecasts of potential aurorae. One of these, "Aurora Watch UK," is based in Lancaster, and this is available for free and is very easy to use. However, as with any type of prediction, sometimes things can go wrong. At 1:25 PM on 23rd August 2016, an aurora alert was issued. This predicted a dramatic auroral surge and a potential auroral storm. This led to a high degree of anticipation for astronomers on and off the Island. Plans were made for trips up to the northern coast that evening. However, a few hours later, at 4:31 PM, an update was published:

"We apologise for the earlier false alert (issues 13:25 UTC today) which was caused by a lawnmower causing a local disturbance at our Lancaster site".

Aurora observing tips

So, just how can you see aurorae for yourself. There are a few basic things that may help you to see this natural but elusive phenomenon.

1. Set your smartphone or computer for auroral alerts and be ready to head out to a suitable location to see this elusive phenomenon.
2. Statistically, the best time to see an aurora is before and after the spring and autumnal equinoxes in March and September. However, a word of cautious optimism, aurorae can often be seen outside these dates.
3. Similarly, a northern horizon will always be the best location to see aurorae, but there can be exceptions. I recall receiving a call from Manx Radio around June 2014 asking what the phenomenon was visible in the western sky. This was a great aurora seen just before the 2014 peak.
4. The peak time to see a dramatic aurora is a few years before and after the peak of the 11-year cycle. Aurorae around this peak tend to be intensive and thus more dramatic. Low key or less intensive aurorae can be seen more or less at any time.
5. Statistically, the best time to see the aurorae is from 10.00 PM to about 2.00 AM.
6. It will always be best to try on a moonless night to see the aurorae. The Moon is a significant source of light pollution, but if it is a clear night, and you have a good clear northern horizon view, then it's always worth having a look.

Having found a suitable location on a moonless night in late March at about midnight, what should you look for?

7. Look at the northern horizon and look for a faint band of what may appear to be white clouds. Then, look very closely and see if there are any stars visible through these "clouds". If you can, then it is undoubtedly an aurora. Once identified, keep watching, and hopefully, it will develop.
8. Another way to identify aurorae is to use a camera. This tip was given to me by an astrophotographer whilst on a cruise, and I could not believe its effectiveness. The human eye does not see as a camera does. So, we can use a camera as an "aurora detector", providing that you have a camera that can vary the speed, aperture and ISO setting. Unfortunately, mobile phone cameras do not have this degree of control. Set your camera onto the widest aperture, the slowest speed and the highest ISO setting. Just point at the area you are observing and take a picture with an exposure time of, say, ten seconds. Then take a look at the captured image, and if it shows any glimpses of green, then it is aurorae beginning to develop, so keep watching!

So, what will you see, and what can you expect? An auroral display will typically start with:

- A faint glow: on the northern horizon, which may well come and go over some time, then an arc may appear. Such a level of activity may last for minutes or for hours.
- Arcs and Bands: can be quiet but suddenly brighten and spread across the sky.
- Patches: can pulse, flash and fade.
- Rays: can appear to shoot across and down from the sky.
- Curtains: Are probably the most spectacular form, especially as they can appear to wave as if blown by some extra-terrestrial wind.
- Corona: Can be seen overhead during auroral storms.
- All-sky colours: Are the most common, especially from the lower latitudes. However, such aurorae only tend to occur at levels above KP 7.

While aurorae displays may be beautiful, they can also have serious consequences on Earth and have been known to cause problems throughout history.

A Kp 9 auroral storm event occurred in 1859 when the "Carrington event" occurred. It was named after the astronomer who observed and reported it. An auroral display lit up night skies worldwide. Very bright aurorae were seen from the Arctic circle to southern areas such as Cuba, Hawaii, and North Africa. It was reported that gold miners in the western US confused the glow with the morning light, woke up and started to get ready for work in the middle of the night. Across North America and Europe, the strength of the solar storm caused a complete failure of telegraph systems. In today's hi-tech age, such an event would be so intense that mobile Wi-Fi networks and mobile data systems would probably have crashed. This could have created a worldwide total communication blackout.

There have been other such events throughout history with many instances of telegraphic interference. For example, during intense auroral activity in 1903 and 1921, fires were reported at telegraph signal stations. In 1967, a blackout of polar surveillance equipment led the US to scramble their nuclear bombers at the peak of the Cold War. Shortly after, the aurora was confirmed as the source. In 1989 a massive blackout caused by an aurora led to a blackout over Quebec and the US North-eastern seaboard. It is recorded that this blackout led to an increase in the birth rate in this region nine months later.

A recent study (2021) looked at sightings of aurorae seen between 30 degrees north or south of the equator. The great storm of September 1770 led to aurorae being visible from lower latitudes for over a week. Drawings have been found from this time showing a sunspot twice the size of the sunspot that caused the Carrington Event of 1859, which was previously thought to have been a singular event. The study by the US Geological Survey suggests that auroral storms occur roughly every 45 to 60 years.

Chapter 9

Eclipses (*Bodjal*) from the Isle of Man and Beyond

In 1966, as a young boy living in Liverpool. I was looking forward to our family summer holiday in the Isle of Man. We stayed in Ramsey at a cottage by the Whitebridge in August and saw the first few of that year's TT races. The races had been delayed due to the earlier seamen's strike. Later that year, I saw my first partial solar eclipse. There had been one in October 1959, but I was just six years old, and I have no recollection of it. In 1966 we had two, in May and September, and I vividly recall the second one.

From my viewpoint, on 22nd September at 10:24 AM, the Sun was 20% eclipsed by the Moon. It was a Sunday, so I was not at school that day. I set up my Charles Frank 4-inch reflecting telescope that I had received as a Christmas present the previous year from my parents. I had learned how to project the solar image through a telescope and I managed to get a photograph of what was, to me, a spectacular event.

I have now managed to see several partial eclipses like the one I saw that September morning from our home in Liverpool. Solar eclipses can be seen as partial in relatively large areas of the Earth, but the view of a total eclipse of the Sun has to be one of the most amazing natural phenomena that can be seen. However, it is not possible to see solar eclipses with the naked eye—

A partial eclipse from Liverpool – 22nd September 1966 at 10.24 AM.

a serious word of warning. **Never** try and look at the Sun with the naked eye and **never** use a pair of binoculars or a telescope to look directly at the Sun. You could cause severe injuries to your eyes and possibly blind yourself. As the late Sir Patrick Moore used to say, *"You only get two chances to look at the Sun, left eye and right eye"*. Always use appropriate solar glasses or approved solar filters.

It has been alleged that Galileo suffered serious eye injuries from observing the Sun through a primitive telescope. However, this is just an urban myth. His blindness occurred 25 years after his initial solar observations and was caused by cataracts and glaucoma.

Solar eclipses

The author's granddaughter Summer Roberts wearing solar glasses.

The Sun is 400 times bigger than the Moon but is 400 times further away. This means that the Moon will appear to be the same size as the Sun as seen from the Earth. When the Moon passes in front of the Sun, a total solar eclipse may be seen from anywhere inside a narrow, central path. This is usually up to about 100 km (62 miles) in width but exceptionally as much

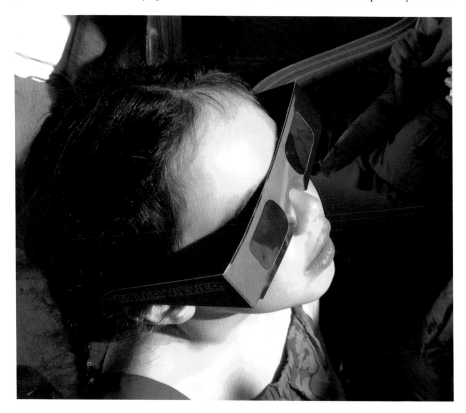

as 260 km (162 miles) wide. Total eclipses can be seen for up to three or four minutes, with a rare maximum possible of just over seven minutes. The length of time such an eclipse will be visible is dependent on the path's location and the actual distance of the Sun and Moon at the time of the eclipse. There will also be a "partial" eclipse on each side of this eclipse path. The actual amount that the solar disc is covered by the Moon will depend upon how far from the central path an observer is located. Sometimes the Moon is slightly further away, and/or the Sun is nearer. Consequently, the Moon does not entirely cover the Sun, so we get an "annular" eclipse. A ring or "annulus" of sunlight is still visible. An annular eclipse has all the timing, location and wonder, but you don't get the spectacular effects of totality, the solar corona, prominences or diamond ring effect.

All eclipses have two distinct types of shadow, the "umbra" and the "penumbra". The umbra is the shadow's dark central or core area. During a solar eclipse, you will see totality if you are within the umbral shadow region, as you will be unable to see any part of the Solar disc. You will, however, only see part of the solar disc in the penumbral shadow region or a partial eclipse.

Lunar eclipses

Total lunar eclipses always occur when the Moon is full, whilst Solar eclipses always occur at a New Moon. Though not as spectacular as solar eclipses, lunar eclipses are still worth seeing. They occur roughly as frequently as their solar equivalent but over a much wider eclipse path. As a consequence, they are seen by many more observers. When the Earth passes between the Sun and the Moon, we see the Earth's shadow on the Moon. This will cause the Moon to turn a distinctive red or coppery colour. This is because red light is refracted (bent) more than blue light, and so the Full Moon will turn a deep red or copper colour. Before and after totality of a lunar eclipse and in the penumbral shadow area, you will see a curved shadow on the Moon or a partial lunar eclipse. In about 450 BC, Anaxagoras observed this curved shadow of the Earth on the Moon and concluded that the Earth was spherical.

There can be a maximum of seven eclipses in one year. This will occur in 2038 when there will be three solar and four lunar eclipses. Most years have four eclipses, two of each, which is the minimum possible. But the narrow corridor of total solar eclipse paths means that they are comparatively rare events. Statistically, they occur at any given place on Earth every 500 or so years.

Solar eclipses have been seen throughout history, and the first recorded eclipse was seen in 2136 BC in China. It was believed that eclipses represented an angry dragon devouring the Sun. Even today, during an eclipse, the Chinese go outside and make lots of noise to frighten the dragon away. It always seems to work. In 2136 BC, the court astrologers Hsi and Ho failed to predict an eclipse and were summarily executed.

Over the last 1,500 years, there have been twelve total solar eclipses visible from the UK but only one from the Isle of Man on 7th March 1598. The eclipse path crossed Ireland and the Isle of Man, but no records exist of this event. During the 1st May 1185 partial eclipse, which was seen by the Monks at Rushen Abbey, the Sun was 92% eclipsed. The dimming of the Sun would have been noticeable even if it had been cloudy.

On 29th June 1927, there was a total eclipse of the Sun close to the Isle of Man. The path of totality went across Liverpool Bay and Lancashire. The local press at the time showed the path of the eclipse but totally ignored the Isle of Man. A great example of the "Miss Isle of Man syndrome". This is the local name given when that the Island is totally missed off the map.

Manx residents could this year have seen a 99% eclipse. However, looking back through the old Manx newspapers, I found this comment:

"The much-boosted eclipse of the Sun took place in the early hours of Wednesday; at all events, it can safely be said as far as the Isle of Man is concerned, that we believe it took place according to the arranged programme. As a spectacle, it was a decided failure, and Southport's "Darker June" effort is now relegated to the past like a damp squib which misfired".

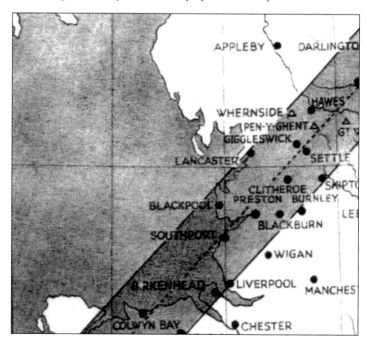

Map showing the 1927 eclipse path. (With the IOM missed off the map).

However, not wanting to pass by a commercial opportunity, the Isle of Man Steam Packet organised a special eclipse excursion on their steamer "Mona". The trip took about 150 potential eclipse spotters from the Island at 11.00 PM the previous night to see the eclipse from Liverpool Bay. They were joined by another Steam Packet vessel, the "Manxman", with a similar group from Liverpool. Despite a poor forecast, the Sun was seen at about 5:15 AM. However, apart from a brief glimpse of the early partial phase at about 5:30 AM, it was too cloudy. Another quote in the local newspaper regarding the excursion stated:

"Those who did not make the trip were rather luckier than those who were on board because as a paying proposition they are most unsatisfactory, at least this one was, as viewed from Liverpool Bay". The writer concluded: *"So ended our trip to see the eclipse, and as there will not be another until 1999, I don't think I will trouble about it".*

However, Manx resident, Percy Johnson writing in the same paper a day or so later, went to see the eclipse at Hillside just outside Southport. He was of a different opinion and wrote:

No description I have ever read, no picture I have ever seen, no mental image I have ever formed can for a moment compare with the actual experience of a total solar eclipse which was my great fortune on Wednesday last. My greatest expectation of this "dread darkness" of totality and of the glory of the corona were completely surpassed. In a few brief seconds, the light of the World went out, and the beautiful but truly "unearthly" vision of the corona met my startled gaze. This rare and stupendous experience was shared by thousands who congregated on the sandhills just outside Southport and held them spellbound while it lasted".

I have been fortunate to see two total solar eclipses so far and could not agree more with Mr Johnson. They really are beyond words

The next eclipse of note from the Isle of Man was in 1954, when Manx residents could have seen a 77% eclipse. Seven years later, in February 1961, there was an 89% eclipse. The total solar eclipse visible in the UK in Cornwall on 11th August 1999 was 88% eclipsed from the IOM. I originally planned to visit Cornwall in 1999, but I was asked to be an "eclipse guide" on a campsite in northern France. This fell through, and I ended up seeing it on television. Perhaps it was just as well, as the weather was poor from both a Manx and Cornish perspective, and very few got to see the eclipse from either the Island or Cornwall. It was, however, seen spectacularly seen from many European locations.

On 3rd October 2005, just after 8.00 AM, an annular eclipse occurred which would have been seen as a 54% eclipse from the IOM. A number of us in the IOMAS made plans to observe this eclipse from our observatory at Foxdale. Unfortunately, the Celtic Sea God, Manannan, must have thought the eclipse was visiting royalty. So, down came his cloak, and we saw absolutely nothing. It was so disappointing. There was, however, to be an exciting sequel. After our aborted attempts to see this eclipse, one of my Isle of Man College night school class attendees from the previous year, Patrick Cowley, sent me details from The Daily Telegraph newspaper advertising a trip to Turkey to see the total eclipse of 29th March 2006. The trip cost just £300, including a return flight to Turkey and an overnight stay in the small town of Side, which was inside the path of totality. This seemed a great opportunity, so I suggested that some of us from the IOMAS might want to go. Eventually, Gary Corlett, Dave Storey and I from the Island booked the trip. We were joined by my brother Graham from Liverpool. We set off for an overnight stay with my brother, and the next day we flew to Antalya in Turkey on 28th March.

The trip was excellent from start to finish, especially when we arrived at the hotel to find a free bar! We had dinner and then had a talk about the eclipse from Ian Morison of Jodrell Bank (who we promptly invited to come to the Isle of Man). After copious amounts of alcohol (it would have been rude to have refused such hospitality), we retired to bed and awaited the following day. The day of the eclipse dawned, and despite some of us feeling a little delicate from the excesses of the night before, we waited with bated breath for "first contact" when the lunar disc first encroaches onto the solar

Gary Corlett, Graham Parkin, the author and Dave Storey at the 2006 Turkish eclipse.

disc. This occurred precisely on schedule, and we watched spellbound. I recall vividly watching the eclipse in awe and amazement. It seemed perfect the way the Sun was precisely covered by the Moon. We experienced the wonders of totality, saw the solar corona, the diamond ring effect and some solar prominences erupting from the solar limb. What was surprising was that as we awaited totality, it was so quiet. Everyone just stood and watched. Once totality finished, it was just one big party. It was a fantastic sight, and I wholeheartedly concur with Percy Johnson, who described such an event perfectly back in 1927 in the Manx newspaper:

"My feeble attempt to describe a total eclipse can never convey to those who were fortunate enough to witness it more than the faintest idea of the impressive grandeur of a phenomenon which is surely unparalleled in Nature".

We returned home that night, tired but full of awe and feeling privileged that we had seen and shared an amazing event that I will remember for the rest of my life. Seeing totality was such a special event that I wanted to share it with Sandra, and I promised her that we would, at the next opportunity, go and see one together.

On 20th March 2015, we had another opportunity to see a partial eclipse when the Sun was 91.5% eclipsed from the Island at 9:32 AM. Those lucky enough to have had clear skies saw just a thin sliver of sunlight below the lunar limb. Through Manx National Heritage, I had arranged to host a breakfast and eclipse watch at the Sound Restaurant. Unfortunately, once again, the weather let us down so instead, I gave a lecture on what might have been seen. As we packed up to come home, the latter stages of the

Totality from Turkey – 20th March 2015.

Dave Storey, Ian Morison, the author and Gary Corlett in Side, Turkey, 20th March 2006.

eclipse were visible, and when I got back home, Sandra met me with the comment: *"Did you see it? I did. I had a great view here in Onchan"*. Oh, the wonders of eclipse chasing!

Further to my personal promise to share a total eclipse with Sandra, in 2014 we met Ron and Gayle Taylor from Murphy, North Carolina, in the US during a cruise to New Zealand. They were astounded when I knew where Murphy was. This was because I knew there would be a total eclipse of the Sun visible from Murphy, North Carolina, on 21st August 2017 and I was hoping to arrange a trip there. They immediately asked us to join them to see it. So, a plan was devised.

We arranged to have a family holiday with our two children, their partners, and our four grandchildren in Florida. We went to see a certain Mr M. Mouse and his friends and did all the theme parks. After the holiday, Sandra and I drove up from Orlando to Bear Paw, Murphy, North Carolina. We met up with Ron and Gayle, and I gave a talk about the eclipse the day before in the Bear Paw community centre. On the morning of the eclipse, the weather was absolutely perfect. We saw the whole of the eclipse from on a dock on Lake Hiwassee. It was again a most moving and awe-inspiring occasion, and this time I was delighted to have had Sandra share it with me. Keen Manx and UK astronomers saw a 4% eclipse at dusk.

There is a poignant tale from this trip. That evening our hosts held a celebratory dinner and spoke about our personal eclipse experiences. One lady, however, came up to me and said she did not see totality. As instructed in the media, she used her eclipse glasses to see the initial partial phase of the eclipse. But she had not realised that you take them off for totality.

Sandra, the author and Ron Taylor in Lake Hiwassee – 21st August 2017.

Above: Totality in the US – 21st August 2017. *(Dave Storey)*

Summer, Tracy and Rio Roberts in Clearwater, Florida – 21st August 2017.

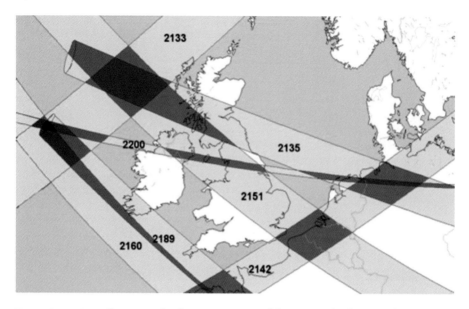

Future eclipse paths over the UK and the Isle of Man 2000 to 2200.

Consequently, she never saw any of the spectacular features of totality.

Seeing the wonders of a total Solar eclipse ought to be on everyone's "bucket list". They are a moving and amazing spectacle. However, if you would like to see one from Manx shores, you will have to wait a few years. The next path of totality to cross the Island will be in 2151, but if it's cloudy, don't worry, there will be another one just 49 years later in 2200. But be careful as this one has a much narrower path of totality.

In the meantime, we will have the biggest partial one for over 100 years on 12th August 2026, when a 92.3% eclipse will be visible to Manx residents. Channel Island residents will see totality in 2081, whilst the UK will see one in 2090.

Manx Lunar Eclipses

I have seen many lunar eclipses on the Isle of Man over the years, and some have been quite spectacular, others less so. It is all to do with the colour that the Moon turns during a total lunar eclipse when the Moon passes through the Earth's umbra or central shadow area. The amount of atmospheric pollution can also affect the red colour quite significantly. On some occasions, the Moon turns deep red in colour, making it almost invisible. In 2010, following some Icelandic volcanic eruptions, the amount of material in the atmosphere caused the lunar eclipse on 21st December 2010 to be much darker than previous ones.

Whilst not as spectacular as the solar variety of eclipses, there have been quite a few notable lunar eclipses. On 1st March 1504, Christopher Columbus used his knowledge of a forthcoming lunar eclipse. He threatened the local populace that he would turn off the Moon if the local natives did not supply him with provisions for his ongoing voyage. They didn't, so he did! The next day he got all the supplies he required.

Lunar eclipses that occur in the early evening tend to be ones most people are most likely to see. So total lunar eclipse's occurring at around 9.00 PM are ideal, with the Moon rising at about 6.00 or 7.00 PM. This will mean the bright Moon will slowly fade in brightness as it moves into the Earth's umbra. This will give the most dramatic and beautiful eclipse. I recall such an eclipse taking place on 7th September 2006 at the IOMAS observatory during our monthly meeting. During my review of forthcoming astronomical activity, I just casually mentioned that: *"if you look out of the windows over there, you might see a lunar eclipse"*.

Two minutes later, the room was empty, and I was talking to myself. It was a wonderful eclipse and one of the most memorable.

I also recall back in 2018, whilst doing a stargazing session on board a ship and being aware that the Moon would rise totally eclipsed. There was a cloud layer on the eastern horizon, and the Moon was not visible. I pointed out the sky above the cloud where the Moon would rise and advised all assembled that the Full Moon would rise, notably darker than usual, being eclipsed. It arose quite dramatically just as I was talking. Despite my

Lunar Eclipse at the IOMAS Observatory – 7th September 2006. *(Dave Storey)*

trying not to take ownership of this magnificent spectacle, I did receive a round of applause.

Lunar eclipses are great to see, but I have to implore all readers, if you get the opportunity to see a total solar eclipse, do so. There is nothing at all like it. As Gary Corlett commented to me during our trip to see the 2006 eclipse in Turkey when I was speechless: *"It takes a lot to keep you quiet"* When it comes to matters astronomical, I have to agree. I have never seen anything quite like it, and I do hope to see a few more in future years.

Transits

A transit occurs when a planet that orbits in between the Earth and Sun passes over the face or disc of the Sun. Only two planets, Mercury and Venus, can transit the Sun as seen from the Earth. We could have seen an Earth/Moon transit from Mars in 1984 and, perhaps by the time of the next one in 2084, we may be able to see such an event?

In 1631 the Italian astronomer Gassendi realised that the two inner planets could, as seen from Earth, pass across the solar disc. It was a significant discovery that helped us understand more about our solar system. Whilst Mercury transits the Sun about 13 or 14 times each century, Venusian transits are much rarer. This is because Mercury is much closer to the Sun than Venus and, consequently, orbits more rapidly. Mercury's year is only 88 days, compared to Venus's 225 days. Therefore, Venusian transits only occur in pairs 8 years apart, every 115 years.

When a transit occurs, it is possible using the projection technique or solar filters to see the event. Mercury and Venus can be seen as black dots moving across the Sun's face. Mercury is, however, much smaller and further away and so will be seen as a small black disc not easily seen. Venus, however, will easily be seen as a distinct black disc moving across the face of the Sun, possibly even through a pair of eclipse glasses

Transits of Mercury always occur in May or November. The last was in 2019, and we shall have to wait until 2032 for the next one. We had a transit of Venus in 2006 and again in 2012. The first observed transit of Venus was in 1639, and there is a great Manx link to it, which was mentioned in chapter two.

In 1639 Jeremiah Horrocks from Hoole, in Lancashire, predicted that a transit of the planet Venus would occur on 24th November. Horrocks advised his friend William Crabtree, and it was Crabtree who was recorded as being the first person to ever see a Venusian transit. If you would like to see a Venusian transit yourself, I am afraid you will have a long wait. They always occur in pairs 8 years apart and the next pair will be in 2117 and 2125.

On 8th June 2006, several IOMAS members met at the society's observatory to see the Venusian transit, only the sixth one ever observed. The weather was mostly kind to us, and we saw the event from the point of ingress onto the solar disc. I thought about possibly seeing the transit from an iconic Manx location. The Great Laxey Mine was highly productive in 1882 at the time of the last transit. So, I persuaded fellow IOMAS members Angela Bridson, Gary Corlett and his 11-year-old daughter Ealish to accompany me to Laxey Wheel. We carried a telescope, tripod and camera up the 96 steps to the viewing platform. We attempted to project the Sun onto a card to see the transit. Alas, it was too hazy, and the attempt failed. However, we returned to the observatory and managed to see Venus egress the solar disc.

On 6th June 2012, the seventh ever observable transit of Venus took place. This one was also visible from the IOM for a short time after sunrise and visible over the eastern Mediterranean and the Middle East. Sandra and I were scheduled to be flying to Dubai to join a cruise when the transit was taking place. Realising this, I made plans to observe it from the aircraft using a handheld telescope. I calculated the transit would be taking place at sunrise from an altitude of 40,000 feet. I made sure I had a window seat on the left-hand side of the plane and sat there anticipating the sunrise. Usually, all the window blinds are down on night flights, and most of the passengers try to get some sleep. Shortly before dawn, I lifted my window blind. As I opened it, one of the flight attendants came hurrying over asking me to close it, as it would probably disturb other passengers trying to sleep. I politely declined, pointing out it would be 115 years until the next Venusian transit. I subsequently managed to project an image using my small telescope and

Transit of Venus
IOMAS Observatory
– 06:35 BST – 8th
June 2006.

Gary Corlett and the author attempting to observe the 2006 transit at Laxey Wheel.

Below left: Transit as seen from 30,000 feet over Iran – 6th June 2012.

Below right: Transit as seen from Dubai – 6th June 2012.

clearly saw Venus on the solar disc. I was also able to see this transit in its latter stages on the quayside, waiting for the ship in Dubai.

Mercurian transits are much more common and not as dramatic as their Venusian counterparts. I have seen a few over the years, but my next-door neighbour Alan Samuels was not impressed. He called around whilst observing the 9th May 2016 transit and asked what I was doing. I showed

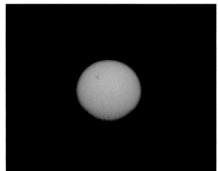

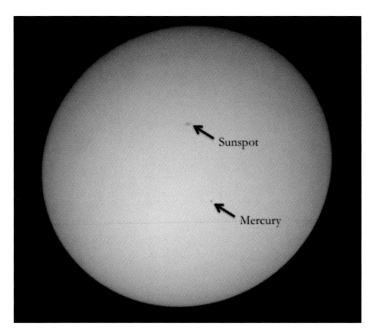

Transit of Mercury –
9th May 2016.
(Graham Gordon)

him the small dot of Mercury transiting the Sun on my projection screen. He was totally underwhelmed. A few months later, he played a joke on me. He called me over with a serious look on his face and a piece of paper in his hand. He showed me a circle drawn on it with a small mark inside it and asked me if it was possibly of interest!

Facebook comment...!

Finally, in 2021 I agreed to do another lecture for MNH at the Sound Visitor Centre for the partial solar eclipse on 10th June. The eclipse was an annular one that would have been seen on the Isle of Man as a 27% eclipse. When the event was advertised. a potential guest asked if it could be moved to a non-school day! Ironically, during what would have been TT race week, the schools were closed anyway. You could not make it up! On the day, the weather was atrocious, and we saw absolutely nothing.

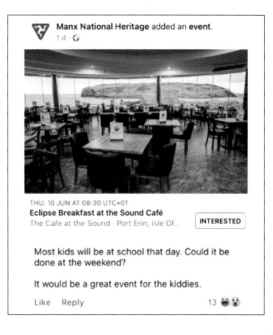

Manx National Heritage added an event.
1 d · 🌐

THU, 10 JUN AT 08:30 UTC+01
Eclipse Breakfast at the Sound Café
The Cafe at the Sound · Port Erin, Isle Of...

[INTERESTED]

Most kids will be at school that day. Could it be done at the weekend?

It would be a great event for the kiddies.

Like   Reply   13 😀😀

Chapter 10

The Manx Christmas Star

Around Christmas time, many people wonder what the Star of Bethlehem might have been and just what may have been visible in the night sky at this time? It is a fascinating subject, one that has been subject to much debate and speculation for over 2000 years. As an astronomer, I have frequently been asked what I thought the "star" might have been.

In late 1996 there were three bright planets in our evening skies, Mars, Venus and Jupiter. Venus, in particular, had been at "elongation", its furthest distance from the Sun in the evening sky on 6th November. It had dominated the early evening sky over Peel in the west for some months. I recall being asked by many people whether this was possibly the "Star of Bethlehem".

One of the first places I visited when I joined MNH was the House of Manannan in Peel. This new heritage centre, which was to become an award-winning "British Isles Museum of the Year," was scheduled to open in July 1997. I was shown, amongst other things, a replica Celtic roundhouse. This reconstruction was based on similar structures that existed on the Island at around 500 BC. It is known that Manx Celts were living on the Island in similar structures around the time of the birth of Christ.

In such roundhouses, the residents would, in the winter months, take

Reconstruction of a Celtic Roundhouse interior at the House of Manannan, Peel, Isle of Man.

everything such as animals, cooking and washing facilities inside. Consequently, there would have been many distinct smells, odours and aromas inside. So, you can imagine the residents going outside for some fresh air on crisp cold frosty nights. There would be very little in the way of light pollution, just the light from fires for cooking and heating.

These hardy early Manx residents would have been able to appreciate the wonders of our dark skies. In addition, they would almost certainly have been able to observe any significant astronomical phenomenon at the time.

We also have written evidence from the Cistercian Monks at Rushen Abbey. In the "Chronicles of Mann and the Isles," they recorded many astronomical observations from the Island, one of the most notable observations being the eclipse in 1185.

This, along with the recent planetary activity, set me thinking. If we consider the various astronomical phenomenon as possible explanations for the Christmas star – just what may have been seen from Manx skies around this time?

The actual "star" is referred to in the Holy Bible in the New Testament, in Matthew chapter two, when it is mentioned four times:

Matthew II, 1–2:

*"Now when Jesus was born in Bethlehem of Judaea in the days of Herod the King behold, there came wise men from the east to Jerusalem, saying, where is He that is born King of the Jews? For we have seen His **star** in the east and are come to worship Him".*

Matthew II, 9–10:

*"Then Herod, when he privily called the wise men, enquired of them diligently when the **star** appeared. When they had heard the king, they departed; and lo, the **star**, which they saw in the east went before them, till it came and stood over where the young child was. When they saw the **star**, they rejoiced with exceeding great joy".*

Any explanation of what was visible back then needs to include all of these references. Many spectacular events can be seen in the night sky, such as comets, eclipses, occultations, conjunctions or supernovae. The telescope was not invented until 1608, so only bright events visible to the naked eye could have been the "star". To see three spectacular and dramatic phenomena in a comparatively short period is difficult to explain.

One significant factor is the actual birth date of Jesus. It is commonly accepted that the birth of Jesus was not on 25th December in the year 1 AD, but he was born sometime earlier. Records show that King Herod died around 4 BC, so the birth has to have been before then.

Considering the various options about just what the "star" may have been. Could it have been…?

Giotto's "Adoration of the Magi".

A Comet

Throughout history, comets have been seen in the night skies. We know Comet Halley appeared in the heavens in 12 BC, so it is not credible as a candidate, and it is most unlikely that this was the Christmas star. No other bright Comets are found in the written records of the time. However, Giotto di Bondone's painting "Adoration of the Magi" shows Comet Halley in the sky above a manger.

It was significant that ESA named their Halley's Comet explorer spacecraft "Giotto" after the fourteenth century Italian Renaissance painter

A Solar eclipse

Using modern computer software programmes, we can ascertain that no total solar eclipses were visible in this period. There was a partial eclipse of the Sun in 6 BC, but it is unlikely that this was the "star".

Jupiter just prior to a lunar occultation.

A lunar occultation of Jupiter

An occultation is the name given to the phenomenon when the Moon or a planet passes over (or occults) a more distant planet or star. Two lunar occultations of the planet Jupiter occurred on 6th March and 17th April 6 BC. It is suggested that one of these events was of such significance that it is recorded on a coin minted in Antioch in Syria in 55 AD. Occultations such as this are quite rare, and it is certainly a candidate for being one of the recorded observations. On 9th March 6 BC, the Moon was Waxing Gibbous, so the disappearance of Jupiter behind the dark lunar limb would have been quite dramatic.

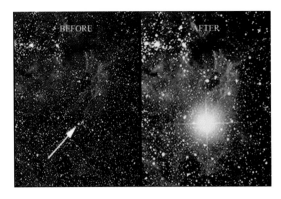

Supernova in the Large Magellanic cloud in 1987. (NASA)

A Supernova or exploding star

Supernovae are caused when giant stars reach a stage in their life cycle when they may become unstable and explode cataclysmically. Such events are spectacular astronomical events and can even be seen for some time in daylight. They have been recorded throughout history and statistically occur in our galaxy at approximately 500-year intervals. The last one seen in the Milky Way was "Kepler's Supernovae" in the constellation Cassiopeia in 1604. We know that there were Supernovae in the constellations of Capricorn and Aquila in 5 BC and 4 BC, respectively. Such phenomena are visible for up to six months and would have been very noticeable and could have a role in the story. In 1987 a supernova was seen in our neighbouring galaxy, The Large Magellanic Cloud. Despite being 169,000 light-years distant, this was easily seen in large telescopes.

A conjunction

Conjunctions occur when two or more planets appear close to each other in the sky. All conjunctions (and eclipses) occur in a path in the sky known as the "ecliptic" This is the path that the Sun, Moon and planets pass along throughout the year. On 17th June 2 BC, there was a conjunction of the planets Venus and Jupiter in the constellation of Leo. A Jewish charm stone from the early AD period illustrates this with the inscription, *"A ruler shall arise from between the legs of the Lion".*

This spectacular conjunction would have been very noticeable to anyone gazing skyward. Despite being one of the more likely options to have been the "Star of Bethlehem," it has one major flaw. As mentioned above, there is historical evidence that Herod died in 4 BC, effectively eliminating this spectacular conjunction as a likely candidate.

Jewish charm stone showing the conjunction in 2 BC.

Venus and Jupiter conjunction from the IOM -13th November 2017.
(Graham Gordon)

A Triple or Great conjunction

Great (or grand) conjunctions occur when the two largest planets in the solar system, Jupiter and Saturn come close to each other in the night sky. Jupiter takes 12 years to orbit the Sun and Saturn 26 years. As a consequence, they pass each other in approximately 20-year intervals. However, all planetary orbits are inclined slightly differently, so the apparent gap between the two planets can vary considerably.

There was a very close "Great Conjunction" on 21st December 2020. These two planets came close together and were just six arc minutes apart. To put this in perspective, the Moon's apparent diameter, as seen from the Earth, is 30 arc minutes. So, Jupiter and Saturn were just 1/5 of the Moon's width apart. This was the closest they had been since 1623, and the view was quite spectacular in Manx skies and throughout the World. Whilst it was cloudy on 21st December 2020, I did see the two very close to each other a few days later on Christmas Eve. I pointed it out to quite a few others before attending a church service. The two were so close that observers on the Island and further afield could see the rings of Saturn and the Moons of Jupiter in the same field of view of a telescope.

The conjunction of Jupiter and Saturn – 21st December 2000. *(Carl Hough)*

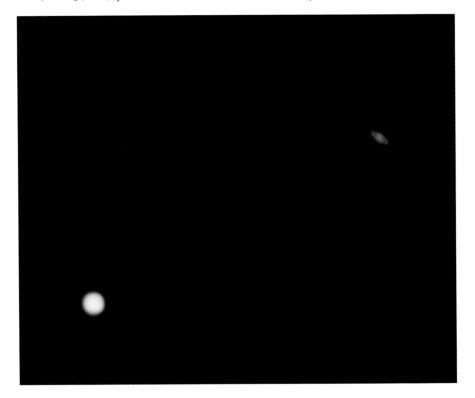

However, another type of "great conjunction" is even more spectacular, but these are quite rare. A "triple great conjunction" occurs when Jupiter and Saturn come close to each other three times in about six months. This repeated coming together is caused by the phenomenon known as "retrograde motion". Observationally, this is when a planet appears to be going in an easterly direction or forward. It then stops and then goes backwards (or retrograde) for a short time before regaining direct or positive motion. The observational characteristics of retrograde motion was a major stumbling block in ancient times in our understanding of the observable characteristics of the Sun's position and our various planets in relation to each other. Initially, it was thought that the Earth was at the centre of the Universe, and everything else, including the Sun, orbited the Earth. Then, in 1543 the Polish astronomer Nicholas Copernicus came up with a radical alternative. He suggested that the Earth actually moved around the Sun. But it took many years for this theory to be widely accepted as correct.

Great triple conjunctions only occur in the constellation of Pisces: The Fish approximately every 900 years. All three components of such a conjunction have significance to those of the Christian or Jewish faith. Pisces has always had religious connotations as one of the zodiacal signs, particularly to those of the Christian faith. The fish (or Ichthus) sign is often drawn or worn by Christians to denote their faith. Jupiter is considered to be a royal or ruler star, and Saturn is, in traditional astrology is seen as the protector of Israel. When Jupiter is visible in our night skies, it is bright and quite unmistakable. While Saturn is not quite as bright, it is still also relatively easy to see.

On the 1st June 7 BC, Jupiter and Saturn came close together in Pisces. Then after a short time, both started going retrograde or backwards. They then came together again on 11th October, before returning to positive or forward motion when they came together again for the final time on 6th December before both moving apart.

If we consider the reports of the star being seen in Matthew's Gospel, the first reference to the star is when they saw it "in the East". Presumably, this was on 6th June 7 BC and could be when the Magi set off for Jerusalem, some 4,000 km (2,500 miles) away. Four months later, in October, they reached Jerusalem and the star "went before them". It then "stood over" Bethlehem two months later on 6th December, when they arrived to pay homage. This may well have been the phenomenon seen all those years ago. The ancient Manx could have also seen it as Pisces is a constellation clearly seen in the autumn Manx skies.

Having considered all of the various possibilities, I have concluded that the Star of Bethlehem was probably this grand triple conjunction. When the two planets Jupiter and Saturn came together in the constellation of Pisces:

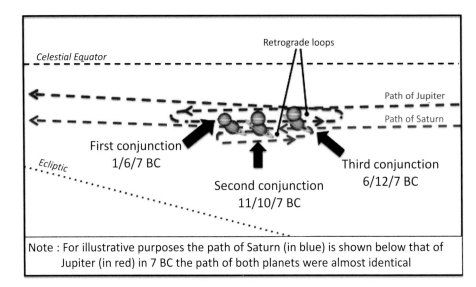

Celestial Equator

Retrograde loops

Path of Jupiter

Path of Saturn

First conjunction
1/6/7 BC

Ecliptic

Second conjunction
11/10/7 BC

Third conjunction
6/12/7 BC

Note : For illustrative purposes the path of Saturn (in blue) is shown below that of Jupiter (in red) in 7 BC the path of both planets were almost identical

The Grand Conjunction of Jupiter and Saturn in 6 BC.

The Fish in 7 BC. The nova in Capricorn also fits into the timeline, so it may well have been a contributory factor.

What is certain is that there was a celestial phenomenon that took place around 2000 years ago. This would undoubtedly have been seen from the Isle of Man, providing that it was not cloudy all the time.

Chapter 11

Astro-cruising

In 2010 as a family, we were considering what we could do for the 90th birthday of my mother-in-law, Ruth Parkinson, on 3rd March 2012. As an experienced traveller, Ruth loved cruising, so we thought a cruise might have merit. We virtually went around the World with her with suggestions. The Mediterranean? (*done that!*), Atlantic crossing? (*done that!*), The Canaries? (*done that!*) Norway? *"Oh, that's an idea, not been there"*. So, a trip on the Fred Olsen's cruise ship, Boudicca, was planned, and we all looked forward to the "Norwegian Winter" cruise in March 2012. There were no thoughts or ideas about the Aurora Borealis or Northern Lights at this stage.

However, I realised that the likelihood of some aurora being visible was a distinct possibility during our cruise. Consequently, I started looking at just what we might be able to see. I learnt that aurora spotting and indeed aurora lecturing was something that many cruise companies offered. I contacted Fred Olsen Cruises and asked them about the possibility of my delivering a lecture for them whilst on board. I was advised that the only "enrichment speakers" they used on board were sourced through the "P and R Agency". I contacted the agency and was invited to attend an interview and audition at their premises near Brighton.

In February 2011, Sandra and I went on holiday to Sri Lanka. So, I arranged to attend the audition before flying out of Heathrow. I nearly did not bother going, but I went along. It seemed to go OK, but the data projector in their office did not work, so I had to do my aurora presentation on my own computer. Halfway through the lecture, I showed a short video of the aurora, which had the song "Northern Lights" by Renaissance playing in the background. At which point the owner of the agency, Peter Rushton, came in and asked: *"why is that great song playing?"* After that, the audition went very well, and I was invited to "go on their books". To do so, I had to pay an enrolment fee of £50. There was also an additional £50 payable upon appointment to a first cruise. I paid the £50 and then went off to Sri Lanka.

Upon my return, I received a telephone call from Peter asking if I would be interested in lecturing for Crystal Cruises. The *Crystal Symphony* ship was sailing from Los Angeles to Hawaii and back in April and they wanted an astronomer enrichment speaker on board. Was I interested? Of course I was, and after managing to get some additional time off work, we flew to LA to join the ship in late April. I was contracted to deliver three lectures during the cruise, and we had a wonderful time. I also offered to do some stargazing sessions on deck. During one of these sessions, I managed to show some guests the ISS, passing over. They all clapped and cheered, so much so I reckon the ISS crew must have heard them from orbit.

In March 2012, we went on the Fred Olsen cruise with Ruth and the rest of the family and we had a great time. We managed to see some aurora on a coach excursion to the northern border of Finland and Norway. It was not particularly spectacular but we were delighted to be able to have seen something.

A few months later, in June 2012, I was asked if I had heard of Mars? I replied, "yes, it's in Leo; why? "No, not that Mars" was the reply, "*the IOM Government "Mutually Agreed Resignation Scheme*" (MARS). Subsequently, in December 2012, I resigned from the IOM Civil Service. The following spring, I set up my own company Astromanx. An astronomy promotional and consultancy company promoting all aspects of astronomy education and outreach. I became heavily involved in setting up the Isle of Man Dark Sky Discovery Sites (see chapter six). My work also includes my lecturing, writing and generally promoting the subject to audiences worldwide.

At Easter 2013, I was invited to undertake a seven-day cruise that summer for Cunard on the *Queen Victoria*. It was a cruise to Norway from Southampton and it was similar to an audition. It went very well, and I was subsequently invited back. It was totally different to the winter cruise I had undertaken to Norway. It was in July, not long after the summer solstice. I recall going for a drink in the nightclub on the ship's upper deck one night. We had a great time and left well after midnight, emerging from the dimly lit lounge into broad daylight!

Amongst the places we visited during this cruise was the magnificent Geirangerfjord, a stunning world heritage site located about 20 km (12 miles) from the Atlantic. When I returned home, I was advised that at the IOMAS monthly meeting, Dave Storey showed a slide showing where I was. The map showed me as being in Norway, nowhere near the sea!

2013 was also the year I became a Fellow of the Royal Astronomical Society (FRAS), and I am grateful to Chris Stott for nominating me. This has proved to be very useful as the Royal Astronomical Society have a special arrangement with Cunard to provide speakers for their three ships, the *Queen Mary*, *Queen Elizabeth* and *Queen Victoria*. In early January 2014, on a cold, wet day in the middle of winter, I was asked if I was available for another trip with Cunard. This time sailing on the *Queen Elizabeth* from Hawaii to Pago Pago in American Samoa in the South Pacific. It did not take too long to accept such a great opportunity. I then received a call from Peter advising that we would not be able to disembark in Pago Pago as there were no flights out of there at that time. Could I possibly stay on and do an additional lecture until the ship arrived in Auckland in New Zealand? That was a tough decision to make. We agreed, went on the cruise, and it was a fantastic experience. All lectures delivered on *Queen Elizabeth* and her sister ship *Queen Victoria* take place in their Royal Court Theatre, modelled extensively on the Gaiety Theatre in the Isle of Man. I understand that a team from Cunard visited the Island during the design stages.

Once onboard, I offered to undertake a few stargazing sessions on deck. The Cruise Director thought this was a great idea and readily agreed. Having agreed on a date and time, I went up on deck the night before to see just what was visible. Well, I did not have a clue about what I was seeing. We were in the southern hemisphere, and not only did I not recognise many of the stars, and the ones I did know were all upside down! Fortunately, I always take with me a small pocket guide to the night sky. I swotted up on the southern stars the next day, and the sessions went well. Fortunately, the stargazing was done looking at the northern sky from the ship's stern as we headed south. I was able to recognise most of the stars, albeit upside down.

When we arrived in American Samoa, I went to the museum in Pago Pago as I had learned they had a sample of Moonrock on display. I was interviewed and ultimately featured in the local Samoan newspaper.

Samoa News – 20th February 2014.

On another *Queen Elizabeth* trip in November 2014, we managed to get

samoa news

| Home | Local News | Sports | Regional | Opinion | Le Lali | Associated Press | Linking Samoans | Our Troops |

Astronomer onboard QE II enriches cruise experience

Thu, 02/20/2014 - 1:27pm | Category: Local News   Show as Latest News

The cruise ship Queen Elizabeth which called into port on Tuesday, Feb 18 brought with it some 2,000 visitors to our shores. Many of the people onboard were from Europe, with several hundred from Great Britain, and as often happens, one of those passengers stopped in to visit Samoa News to say hello.

This particular visitor hailed from the Isle of Man, located in the North Irish Sea between England and Ireland, and he introduced himself as Howard L.G. Parkin, Astronomy Consultant and Guest Lecturer onboard the ship.

Visiting guest lecturer from the cruise ship, the Queen Elizabeth, Howard Parkin, a Fellow of the Royal Astronomical Society and a resident of the Isle of Man. The cruise ship was in Port on Tuesday as part of their round the world cruise. [photo: tlh]

Since 2004, Parkin has been chairman of the Isle of Man Astronomical Society, a non-profit organization which promotes the science of astronomy through lectures and visits, and which also maintains their local Observatory.

Stargazing on board the *Queen Elizabeth*.

Sandra's Mum, Ruth, to come as a passenger. We had a wonderful time with her. Ruth attended all of my lectures and as she was in a wheelchair, she sat at the back of the Royal Court theatre. The lights mean that I can't see the audience whilst I am on stage, but I could see Mum silhouetted against the lit corridor at the back. I noticed she was nodding off, but she told me she heard every word. *"I was just resting my eyes"*, she said. On the same trip, I managed to do some stargazing sessions on deck. As we were in the northern hemisphere, I was familiar with the various features in the night sky above the ship.

During the trip, I was approached by a chap who just wanted to say "Hi" He was a fellow Parkin. Michael, who lived in Sydney, Australia. In January 2016, whilst on holiday in Australia, we met up with Michael and his wife. We enjoyed some time with them in Sydney. It turned out that their son David and daughter Kate Ede are opera singers and we managed to see them in *the "Barber of Seville"* at the Sydney Opera House. It was a marvellous experience.

It was during another Cunard trip that I had my biggest ever audience. In April 2015, we were on a transatlantic voyage from New York to Southampton. I was doing my "Meteors and Comets" lecture and noticed that I had a large audience. More and more people were coming in. By the time I got to the end of my lecture, there was standing room only with over 700 guests attending. It was then the penny dropped! The next speaker on straight after me was Terry Waite OBE, who spoke about his time in captivity. The reality was that I was his warm-up act!

One other aspect of lecturing on astronomy on cruise ships is the interesting people you meet. On numerous occasions following my lectures, guests come up to me and thank me for my lectures. Often they tell me of their own involvement in the space programme. As most cruises tend to have many US guests on board, I tend to chat with guests with various space connections. I have met Werner von Braun's doctor, Richard Branson's private pilot, and Roger Chaffee's schoolmate, to name just a few.

One dubious story I recall was when I met a guest who thanked me for my lecture about the lunar landings. We were chatting, and he suddenly told me, *"You do know the Moon is hollow, and it's full of aliens planning an invasion?"* I just commented *"really"* and bid myself a hasty retreat.

One subject that has always fascinated me is the Hubble Space Telescope (HST) story. I have heard some fantastic stories about it. How a ladybird somehow managed to get into the "clean room" where it was being assembled and was found just sitting on the highly polished mirror's surface. This led to a protracted debate on removing it without damaging the mirror's surface. I learnt a plan was made, which involved a suction device being lowered onto the area just above the ladybird. After making a decision, they returned to the mirror. They then discovered that the ladybird had just flown off and was never seen again! Another story about the HST was the time and money it took to decide how to coat the mirror's surface. It took very little time to do the actual coating, but the cost of applying a layer of 65 nanometres (nm) of aluminium and a protective coating of 25nm of magnesium fluoride made it one of the more costly parts of the HST's construction.

One of my most poignant memories was when I had just delivered my Mars lecture and was approached by a guest. He had been one of the flight controllers at the Jet Propulsion Laboratory (JPL) when Mariner 4 had undertaken the first-ever flyby of Mars in 1965. He told me that all of the JPL controllers for the mission were presented with a certificate and copy of an image of Mars from the spacecraft. It was an honour to have met one of the scientists contributing to the programme. I was even more delighted when I returned home, to find he had sent me a copy.

In 2017 I joined a cruise on the Viking Star, sailing from Puerto Rico to Barcelona. We had to fly in a day earlier, and I realised that this would allow Sandra and I to visit the Arecibo Radio Telescope based on the Island. So, I contacted them and arranged a visit. I hired a car, and early on the morning of 25th February, we set off on the 96 km trip from San Juan to Arecibo.

We had a wonderful visit and learnt so much about the telescope. We also got to hear that the actor about Pierce Brosnan, during the filming

Sandra and I at the iconic Arecibo Radio Telescope in Puerto Rico.

of "GoldenEye", was reluctant to run around the perimeter due to the heat and humidity. Having been there, I can understand just how he felt! With much regret, I, along with many other astronomers throughout the World, witnessed the dramatic collapse of this iconic telescope in December 2020.

Following this cruise. I received a call from a one of the Director's of Viking Cruises, asking about them about placing an observatory or a planetarium onboard their new Viking Orion and Viking Jupiter cruise ships. The Godmother of the Viking Orion was to be the former NASA astronaut Anna Fisher. The idea was to give the Orion ship an astronomical theme. They ultimately decided to install a planetarium on both ships, and they wanted to appoint a resident astronomer on board for every cruise these two ships were undertaking. This led to my appointment as the first Viking Resident Astronomer (VRA). This involved my writing two specific lectures for them, which would be presented on each cruise by myself or another VRA. I was also invited to go on a training course at Evans and Sutherland in Salt Lake City, USA, to learn how to write programmes for the onboard Digistar 6 planetarium. Upon my return, I wrote a series of programmes featuring the night sky at various dates and locations worldwide.

We were on the Viking Orion in 2018 in the Mediterranean and met up with Tony Pass from Baldrine, who I used to work with at MNH. He was on holiday in Venice. We met up and had a great time. When we departed, Tony managed to photograph us "flying the flag" as we sailed slowly past St Mark's square and out into the Adriatic Sea.

We joined the Viking Orion for her shakedown, VIP and maiden cruises around the Mediterranean. The VIP cruise was particularly memorable as the Viking Orion's naming session took place during this cruise. The spectacle of the naming ceremony in Livorno, Italy, will stay with Sandra and me forever. What made this trip even more special for me was that Anna Fisher had invited many former astronaut colleagues to join her on the Viking Orion. Over 25 astronauts from NASA and ESA joined us on board. This included our own "Manx" astronaut Nicole Stott and her husband Chris and son Roman. Delivering one of my two VRA lectures on the history of manned spaceflight entitled "NASA, Working with the right stuff" to an audience comprising many individuals who contributed to that history was a surreal and humbling experience. In addition, one evening, there was a "Explorations in Space – A conversation" event. Twenty-one of these astronauts assembled on stage spoke of their experiences and held a question-and-answer session. Before the event started, Chris Stott called me over and suggested I stood in front of the stage and let him take my picture. This is one of my prized photographs from that trip.

Upon our return, I received an email advising me to look at the latest online version of Time Magazine. I found it, and it was a write up about the Viking Orion and its onboard planetarium.

In 2019, we went on another trip on the Viking Orion, this time from Hong Kong to Japan and then onto Alaska. This was a trip that took us across the International Dateline, and as a consequence, we gained a day. The actual day in question was Tuesday 14th May, and so the only way to keep the

Flying the flag on the *Viking Orion* in Venice.

The author in the foreground with 15 flown astronauts who, between them, have made 32 trips into space, travelled over 10,000 orbits of the Earth and spent over 650 days in space!

calendar correct is to have the same day and date twice. I was scheduled to deliver my "Meteor" lecture that day. A guest came up to me a few days before the first 14th and asked, *"When are you doing your Meteor lecture?"* to which I replied, *"Tuesday at 6.30 PM,"* she then asked, *"yes, but which Tuesday"*. You could not make it up!

I thoroughly enjoy my lecturing on the subjects of astronomy and spaceflight, be it to a school group on the Isle of Man, a local WI, to my evening class attendees, on a cruise or to an audience of astronauts. I never dreamt that I would get such an opportunity. I hope that my experiences and enthusiasm might inspire others to reach for the stars.

TIME | GREATEST PLACES 2018

Viking Orion – Cruise ship

Cruisegoers looking for an out-of-this-world experience will find one aboard the Orion, a new space-themed cruise ship that features a planetarium (the most advanced on an ocean ship), a collection of vintage NASA photographs and a resident astronomer, Howard Parkin, who leads lectures and stargazing sessions. The ship began its maiden season navigating the Mediterranean this summer. —

Time Magazine feature – September 2018.

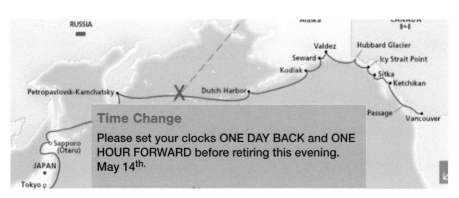

Time Change

Please set your clocks ONE DAY BACK and ONE HOUR FORWARD before retiring this evening. May 14th.

The instructions received onboard on the evening of 14th May 2019.

Chapter 12

Observing the Manx night sky

Living on an Island in the middle of the Irish Sea does have some great advantages from an astronomical perspective. When the sky is clear, it can be quite stunning with very little in the way of light pollution. We can see so much more than our neighbours on the adjacent Isles.

Solar and Sidereal days

Many casual observers do not realise that the stars and the various objects move quite appreciably in our skies. There is a distinctly seasonal nature to the sky. This movement occurs because the Earth turns daily on its axis and also orbits around the Sun. The "Sidereal" day is the time it takes to return to the same position relative to the stars. (Marked as "B" on the diagram below). The "Solar day" is the time the Earth turns precisely once on its axis in relation to the Sun and returns the same position facing the Sun. (Marked as "C" on the diagram below). As well as rotating on its axis, the Earth also orbits the Sun. In 24 hours, it will move approximately 1/365th on its orbital passage around the Sun. The consequence of the difference is that the stars will appear to rise 3 minutes and 55.6 seconds earlier each day.

Sidereal and Solar days.

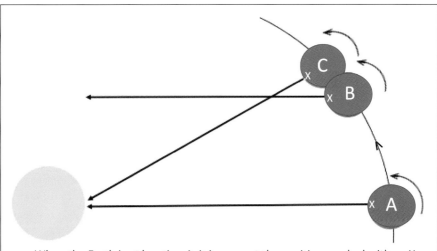

- When the Earth is at location A, it is noon at the position marked with an X.
- One sidereal day later, Earth has rotated once and moved along its orbit to position B.
- For it to be noon again, Earth has to continue rotating for just under 4 minutes to position C to complete a solar day

Opposite: The Milky Way over "Snuff the Wind" mine – 1st November 2018.
(Ron Strathdee)

It is straightforward to prove this for yourself. On a clear night, go outside and look in a southerly direction for a bright star (but not a planet) near the horizon. Line this star up with a feature on your local horizon, a tree, chimney pot, or even a stick, and remember the feature used. The following night go outside about 5 minutes earlier. Look at the same star from the same location and you will notice that it will be in precisely the same spot a fraction under 4 minutes earlier. If it's cloudy, the same technique will work the next day, but it will now be 8 minutes earlier and so on. This seasonal nature of the sky means that if you look for the same feature in the sky over a few days or weeks, you will quickly notice that the sky clearly moves from east to west.

The Milky Way *(Raad Mooar Ree Gorree)*

From our Island home, on a clear moonless night, the Milky Way can be a most impressive sight. Unfortunately, it is often invisible to astronomers on the adjacent islands due to excessive light pollution. The Milky Way varies in its location on a seasonal basis but is always somewhere in our night sky. A few years ago, I was outside during a clear night at one of the IOMAS "Pie in sky" events at the top of Snaefell. I was pointing out various features in the night sky with some of my fellow society members. A lady came up to me and said, "*What a wonderful night, but it's a shame about that big patch of cloud overhead*". I responded: "*Well, actually, that patch of cloud is the Milky Way*".

Twinkling

All the stars in the night sky are so far away that they only appear as points of light, which is why stars twinkle or "scintillate" to use the proper name. They twinkle quite dramatically, especially when seen close to the horizon when they seem to flash different colours. This is caused by the star's light passing through a thicker layer of the Earth's atmosphere. Stars higher up in the sky twinkle but not by as much. The brightest star in our night sky, Sirius, can be seen in the winter months close to the horizon. It is a star that twinkles dramatically and being so bright, it is very noticeable. Planets may appear to look like bright stars, but being much nearer to us, they are actually tiny disks, so they do not twinkle.

Magnitude

On a cold clear night, the twinkling stars look magnificent. However, it does not take long for even a casual observer to realise that not all stars are the same brightness. This caused astronomers considerable difficulty many years ago.

Astronomers use the word "magnitude" to describe a star's brightness. This brightness was defined as its "magnitude of importance" by the Greek astronomer Hipparchus in 150 BC. Hipparchus gave all of the bright stars a magnitude of one, stars half as bright are magnitude two, and so on down to magnitude six, which is the limit of typical naked eye visibility. In 1830 John Herschel (the son of William who had discovered the planet Uranus back in 1761) measured stellar magnitude more accurately. He found that the first magnitude stars are a hundred times as bright as those of the sixth magnitude. Herschel also realised that a few stars are brighter than magnitude one. Using his calculations, he realised that the brightest star in the night sky, Sirius had to be classed as being at a negative magnitude of minus 1.4. Using this same scale, the Sun is at magnitude minus 26.8, and the Full Moon is at minus 12. Both Venus and the ISS can be brighter than magnitude minus 4. Negative magnitudes are customarily written as -1.4 or -4.0 etc. A plus sign is not generally used for stars of positive magnitudes of 0 or fainter. Herschel also discovered that in reality, the original idea of stars being half (or twice) as bright works out as $2.512^{5,}$ which equals 100.0226. This effectively makes the scale a logarithmic one.

Some stars vary in their magnitude and are classed a "variable stars". This is caused by one of two distinct reasons.

"Extrinsic" variable stars are caused when a fainter star passes in front of a brighter one. This is similar to an eclipse, except being so far away, it's just a point of light that changes in its brightness. The most well-known of these is the star Algol in the constellation of Perseus: The Hero. Algol drops by a very noticeable 1.3 magnitudes every 68 hours. This variability was explained by ancient astronomers as being an eye that "winked".

The other type of variable stars are "intrinsic" variable stars, caused when a star has an internal process that can cause the actual output of the star to vary. While minor changes in the brightness of some stars are not uncommon, a few vary dramatically. One such example is the star Mira in the constellation of Cetus, which drops by over approximately eight magnitudes in an 11-month cycle.

Constellations *(Rollageagh)*

A constellation is a group of stars that appear to be relatively close to one another. There are a total of 88 constellations in our skies. However, from our latitude, the most we can ever see is 52. Initially, 48 constellations were recognised and published by the Greek Ptolemy (100-170 AD) in his "Almagest" The list comprised most of today's well-known constellations. In 1930 the International Astronomical Union formally recognised and agreed on 88 constellations and their specific boundaries.

I often get asked about the shapes of constellations and why they are

	Name	Constellation	Season	Magnitude	Distance (ly)
1	Sirius	Canis Major	Winter	-1.46	8.6
2	Canopus	Carina	Southern	-0.75	310
3	Rigil Kentaurus	Centaurus	Southern	-0.27	4.4
4	Arcturus	Bootes	Spring	-0.05	37
5	Vega	Lyra	Spring	0.00	25
6	Capella	Auriga	Winter	0.08	42
7	Rigel	Orion	Winter	0.10	860
8	Procyon	Canis Minor	Winter	0.34	11
9	Achernar	Eridanus	Southern	0.46	140
10	Betelgeuse	Orion	Winter	0.50	640
11	Hadar	Centaurus	Southern	0.61	350
12	Altair	Aquila	Summer	0.76	17
13	Acrux	Crux	Southern	0.76	320
14	Aldebaran	Taurus	Winter	0.86	65
15	Antares	Scorpio	Summer	0.96	600
16	Spica	Virgo	Spring	0.97	260
17	Pollux	Gemini	Winter	1.14	34
18	Fomalhaut	Sthn Fish	Autumn	1.16	25
19	Deneb	Cygnus	Summer	1.25	2,600
20	Mimosa	Crux	Southern	1.25	350
21	Regulus	Leo	Spring	1.39	77
22	Adhara	Canis Major	Winter	1.50	430
23	Shaula	Scorpio	Summer	1.62	700
24	Castor	Gemini	Winter	1.62	52
25	Gacrux	Crux	Southern	1.64	88
26	Bellatrix	Orion	Winter	1.64	240
27	Elnath	Taurus	Winter	1.65	130
28	Miaplacidus	Carina	Southern	1.69	110
29	Alnilam	Orion	Winter	1.69	2,000
30	Regor	Vela	Southern	1.72	840

Note: All stars marked Southern are not visible from Manx Skies

called what they are. It's purely a product of our imagination. Remember when most of the constellations were named, books, if they existed, were only for the privileged and wealthy. Videos, DVD's and photographs did not exist. Hence, people made up shapes and stories about what they could see. It is due to a phenomenon known as "pareidolia". Seeing a meaningful image in a seemingly random or unambiguous pattern. It applies not just to

Table 2. The 30 brightest stars.

constellations but also to seeing shapes in clouds, the Man in the Moon, and the canals on Mars.

I like to think of some ancient Manx residents sitting in a field on a clear night, huddled together and telling stories. One of them points out a group of stars and says: *"Do you see that group over there. It looks like a bull to me. What do you think?"* There was minimal light pollution all those years ago, so they would have great views of the night sky. People are often amused about just how the shapes seen can be identified as a Lion, Bull, Hunter or Dog. However, we are just as bad today. If you look at a map or photograph of Italy, inevitably, you will say it looks like a boot. Just how can a large landmass in the sea possibly be a boot?

Asterisms

As well as constellations, we also have "asterisms" like the Plough in the night sky. If a shape is commonly recognised, which is just part of a particular constellation, or may include stars from more than one constellation, we call this an asterism. Asterisms are unofficially named star patterns chosen to represent familiar objects. Most constellations do not look very much like the object they are meant to represent. Some modern versions or parts of constellations could be said to be asterisms. However, many asterisms fail to catch on, but a few are popularly accepted and are used to help us make sense of the night sky. The most famous asterism is the "Plough," which comprises seven bright stars of the larger constellation of Ursa Major: The Great Bear. On occasions, I have confused US residents whilst talking about the asterism of the Plough. They look at me blankly when I talk about it. They know it as the "Big Dipper". There are many asterisms, some well-known and some obscure. We have a winter hexagon, a winter triangle, a summer triangle, the square of Pegasus, the keystone of Hercules, the belt of Orion, and the coat hanger. Asterisms can also be dependent upon your location on the Earth. The Aborigines and Maoris see a distinctive asterism of the "cooking pot", an upside-down Orion. Perhaps someone can come up with a Manx three legs?

Sometimes we recognise shapes (or asterisms) more familiar and appropriate for modern times. There are quite a few newer ones. In particular, when I deliver my constellations lecture, I like to talk about two distinctive asterisms within the constellations of Sagittarius: The Archer *(Y Sideyr)* and Capricorn: The Sea-Goat *(Y Goayr)*. These constellations are visible in our Manx summer skies low in the southern sky. I prefer to use modern asterisms for these two. It does not take much imagination to see Sagittarius as an old-fashioned teapot and Capricorn as the bottom half of a bikini.

The signs of the zodiac and the ecliptic

The seasons on the Earth are caused by the fact that the Earth's axis is tilted at an angle of 23.5 degrees from the equator. This tilt (or inclination) means that the Sun, Moon, and planets appear to travel along throughout the year along an imaginary line in the sky called the "ecliptic". As the Sun passes along the ecliptic throughout the year, it passes through a total of twelve constellations. These are collectively known as the "signs of the zodiac".

The constellation which the Sun is passing through at the time of your birth is your own individual birth sign (or zodiacal constellation). As the Sun is actually passing through your birth sign, it means that your own birth sign is in the daylight sky at this time, and therefore will not be visible in the evening sky on your birthday. As a result, you only see your zodiacal sign about six months before or after your birthday.

However, due to a phenomenon known as the "precession of the equinoxes," the dates that the Sun actually passes through your own birth sign are actually about a month out. So, for example, if you are born on 3rd August, you might think your birth sign is Leo. However, in reality, the Sun is still passing through the neighbouring constellation of Cancer on that date. Furthermore, there is actually a thirteenth sign of the zodiac (Ophiuchus: The Serpent Bearer), which astrologers conveniently ignore. Therefore, strictly speaking, if you are born between 30th November and 18th December, your sign ought to be Ophiuchus, not Capricorn which in traditional astrology applies to anyone born between 22nd November and 21st December.

Astronomy and astrology used to have much stronger links. However, in the 16th and 17th centuries, Copernicus, Kepler, Galileo, Newton and others proved that the Earth went around the Sun. Rather than the previously accepted theory that the Sun, Moon and other planets orbited the Earth. Consequently, the two subjects went their separate ways, albeit with a common link. (See chapter 18)

The Pole star *(Rollage Hwoaie)*

When looking towards the northern horizon, it becomes apparent that the sky appears to revolve about a specific point in the sky after a short period of short time. This point is called the "northern celestial pole" (NCP). Quite close to the NCP is a star called Polaris, often called the Pole or North star. If you stood at the geographical north pole, the NCP would be directly over your head. However, if you moved to the equator, the NCP would be on your northern horizon. From the Isle of Man or anywhere at a latitude of 54 degrees north Polaris will always be 54 degrees directly above the northern horizon. Using this information, we can find north. All we need to do is to identify which star is Polaris.

Two stars enable us to find Polaris quite easily. The two stars at the bowl end of the asterism of the Plough. are called Merak and Dubhe. From our observing location, if you extend a line from Merak to Dubhe about three times the distance between them, you will arrive at Polaris or the NCP. However, what complicates the issue is that the stars appear to rotate around the NCP. Thus, the Plough will sometimes appear to be sitting just above the northern horizon. At other times it will be standing on its tail or maybe seen directly overhead. This effect proves to us that the Earth spins on its axis. It also indicates the passing of the seasons or, more correctly, the Earth's passage on its yearly orbit around the Sun.

On a clear starry night, find the Plough and the two pointer stars of Merak and Dubhe and Polaris for yourself. Hold your arm with your fist upright in front of you. The upright fist represents approximately 10 degrees. Measure how many fists high the star Polaris appears to be above the horizon. You will find that Polaris is roughly five and a half "fists" height above the northern horizon or approximately 55 degrees. So close to the Isle of Man's latitude of 54 degrees north, this is one of the fundamental principles of celestial navigation. So, if your sat-nav system fails, or you forget it, you can always use the stars to find north and your latitude unless, of course, it's cloudy.

Next time you are on an IOM Steam Packet vessel crossing the Irish Sea, and it's clear, go up on deck and find Polaris for yourself and note its height above the horizon. It should stay more or less in that location throughout your passage. If it gets appreciably lower or higher, it is either very rough, or the Captain has decided to take a detour.

As the skies darken earlier on autumn nights, the Plough will appear to be sitting on the northern horizon as soon as it goes dark. Three months later, in winter, the Plough will appear to be standing on its tail to the right-hand or eastern side of the star Polaris. In spring the Plough will be directly overhead. In summer it will be on the left hand side of Polaris, heading back down towards the northern horizon. This is why casual stargazers *(Rollagedyr)* who can identify the Plough in the autumn months think it has disappeared in spring. It hasn't disappeared; it's just directly overhead.

This seasonal variation can also be seen in one evening. The Plough will be on the northern horizon at 9.00 PM. in autumn. Look towards the north horizon at 3.00 AM, and you will see that the Plough is now standing on its tail in its winter position. The same is valid throughout the year. The Plough will be standing on its tail at 9:00 PM. in mid-winter. Six hours later, at 3:00 AM, it will appear directly overhead.

This apparent rotation of the sky is caused by two factors: The Earth spinning on its axis for 24 hours and travelling around the Sun in one year.

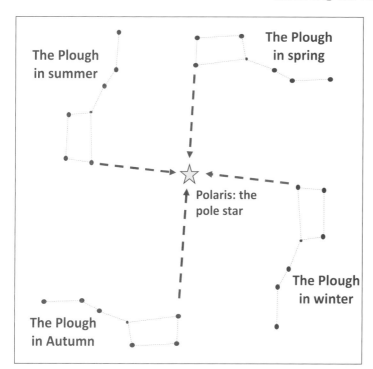

The seasonal rotation of the Plough.

The chart above shows this seasonal effect of the Plough's rotation around the Polaris. A few hours of observation will clearly show the rotational effect of the Plough moving around the NCP. Now turn around and look at the southern sky. The impact of this rotation is far more pronounced. We get a succession of the seasonal constellations transiting across our southern sky, which again can be identified on a seasonal basis.

The Celestial Equator

We have another imaginary line in the sky, the celestial equivalent of the Earth's equator, the "celestial equator". If you were standing at the north pole, the celestial equator would be at your horizon in every direction. If you were standing at the equator, the celestial equator would be directly overhead and run east to west.

When we look at the night sky, we are looking at half or 180 degrees of the entire celestial sphere. Polaris, the pole star, is always 54 degrees above the northern Manx horizon. The celestial equator will always be 90 degrees from the pole star. If we turn around and face south, this leaves 36 degrees (180-(54+90) = 36) of sky between the celestial equator and the southern horizon. This is why we only get to see a certain number of constellations. Any star that appears in the south in autumn will only be visible, providing its location in the sky is higher than 36 degrees south of the celestial equator. Stars and constellations located between 54 degrees north and 90 degrees north will be seen all of the time from the Isle of Man or similar latitudes. This is called the "circumpolar sky". Throughout the year, we can see at least part of 52 constellations. The remaining 36 of the 88 constellations can never be seen from Manx shores.

The circumpolar sky is unique to a specific geographical latitude. All visible stars will be circumpolar at the North Pole, whilst there are no circumpolar stars at the equator. From our location, at 54 degrees north, we see both circumpolar and seasonal constellations. Those visible all year in the northern sky are called the "circumpolar constellations". The seasonal constellations are defined as those visible in the south at 10:00 PM. In September, we see the autumn constellations. In December, the winter constellations, March the spring constellations, and finally in June (although it won't be dark enough) the summer constellations. This seasonal variation can also be seen throughout the night six hours later in one season, as mentioned previously.

The Celestial sphere.

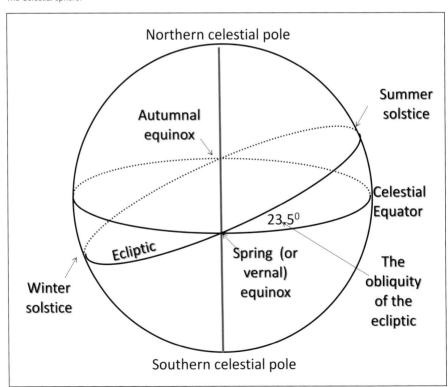

The Green Flash *(Soilshey-bio)*

In all my years observing, there is one phenomenon that I have failed to see despite numerous attempts. The "Green Flash" can be seen just as the solar limb disappears or appears at sunset or sunrise, respectively. At the moment the solar disc disappears or reappears, there can be a quite distinctive flash of vivid green light, which is visible for less than a second.

Living in the Isle of Man, we have fantastic horizon views, and so both sunrise and sunset can be seen on many occasions. However, I have never seen it, but I am aware of many who have. I have often tried to see it whilst cruising but again to no avail. The green flash is known as the "Living Light" (*Soilshey-bio*). Apparently, if you see it at the moment of sunrise, it may give you some of the "living" energy of the Sun. You may be bestowed with some form of "second sight." According to Manx legend, a glimpse of this rare phenomenon gives the viewer the ability to predict events such as a forthcoming fishing boat wreck and the possible loss of life. Other legends advise that if the light from the green flash falls upon certain herbs, which, if they are harvested straight afterwards, may provide special powers. Furthermore, if ingested, they may provide considerable health benefits.

Observing tips

If you want to go stargazing, I can give you a couple of tips that will help enhance your experience.

When we get a clear night, it can be quite cool, even on a late summer evening and when outside, you cool down quite quickly. So, wrap up warm, with layers on. Gloves and hats can be very useful. The nature of stargazing is that you don't move about very much. As a consequence, you cool down quite quickly. It's not so bad in spring, summer and autumn, but the winter can be quite cold. Winter is, however, the best time of the year to do astronomy, as the cold, crisp nights make the stars look stunning.

I recall one winter's evening taking my college class up to one of our 26 Dark Sky Discovery Sites at Conrhenny. We were doing some stargazing on a very cold evening, and we even had some snow on the ground. After about 45 minutes of showing the group the various features of the winter sky, we were all freezing. As the course tutor, I felt I ought not to be the first to suggest we leave. So, we went around the sky again, and we all continued to freeze. Eventually, at about 10.00 PM, I said it was time to go, *"Oh! Thank you,'* said one of the group. *"I did not want to be the first to suggest leaving"* I have learnt from that experience, and we only stay for about 30 minutes or so depending on the weather.

Another tip for stargazing is remembering to get "dark adapted". It takes about 15 minutes or so for your eyes to adjust to the darkness and see fainter objects. When the lights are quickly put on in a darkened room, we shield our eyes and blink until our eyes get used to the bright lights. This is caused by the eye's iris partially closing to let in less light. The opposite occurs when we go outside into a dark location when stargazing. The iris opens up to allow in more light. This is not as much of a problem if there is a bright Moon. If, however, it's a dark moonless night, give your eyes time to get used to the dark. If you want to look at a book or chart, then have a red 'light" torch with you, as red light does not affect your eyes as much as white light.

I recall many years ago, I had been happily stargazing outside in my back garden for about an hour when suddenly the kitchen light was turned on. A well-intentioned individual came to the door and asked me if I would like a cup of coffee. My response has oddly led to my never being asked ever again!

If you are stargazing and your eyes have become dark-adapted, and you realise that a vehicle is approaching, just turn your head away from the lights or simply close your eyes until it has gone. I would also suggest that any stargazing location be well away from a road. If you observe in a car park, I always recommend wearing light-coloured clothing or even a Hi-Viz vest or jacket so you can be easily seen.

Chapter 13

The Northern Night Sky

The constellations of Ursa Major and Ursa Minor are both circumpolar, as seen from a latitude of around 50 degrees north. Another circumpolar constellation can be found by following the line from two "pointer" stars of Merak and Dubhe in Ursa Major beyond Polaris a similar distance again. Slightly to the side of this line, there is a distinct bright five-star group of stars in a "W" or "M" configuration. This is the constellation of Cassiopeia: The Queen. Next to her is a much fainter but similarly sized constellation, Cepheus: The King. The two bears and this royal couple make up the principal constellations in the northern circumpolar sky. There is another faint circumpolar constellation, Draco: The Dragon, but this comprises only 3 stars brighter than the 3rd magnitude. Two of the brightest stars in the sky Capella (6th brightest), in Auriga: The Hunter, and Deneb (19th brightest), in Cygnus: The Swan, are also circumpolar from this latitude.

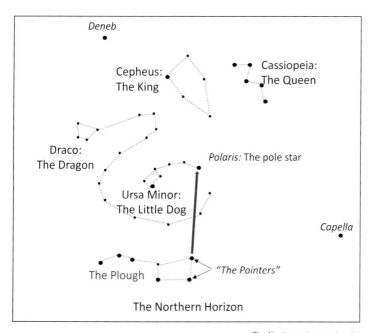

The Northern circumpolar sky.

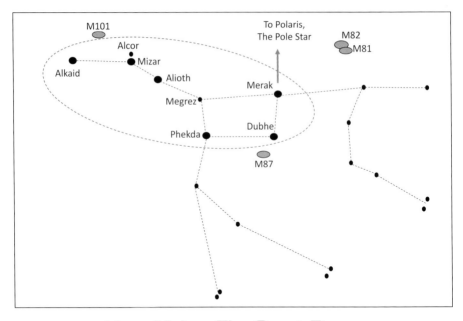

The constellation of Ursa Major, The Great Bear.

Ursa Major: The Great Bear
(Y Mucawin Mooar)

Ursa Major is one of the most recognisable of all the constellations and the 3rd largest in the night sky. The seven stars that make up the Plough asterism contain the six brightest stars within the constellation. A casual view of this asterism will quickly identify Megrez as the faintest. The Plough asterism is also known as the "Big Dipper", "The Wagon", or "King Charles' wain".

The brightest star in Ursa Major is Alioth at magnitude 1.76. The two pointers, Merak and Dubhe, are magnitudes 2.37 and 1.79, respectively. Alkaid at the opposite end of the Plough shines at 1.85 magnitude

Mythologically, Ursa Major represents Callisto, the daughter of King Lycaon of Arcadia. Callisto's beauty surpassed that of the Goddess Juno, who turned Callisto into a bear. Sometime later, Arcas, Callisto's son, was hunting. He was about to kill his mother (as a bear) when Jupiter intervened and swung both Callisto and Arcas (Ursa Minor) into the sky. This is why they both have such long tails.

Throughout history, many cultures have recognised Ursa Major as a bear. However, only the native Americans realised that bears do not have such large tails. Their legend states that the tail is made up of three of their tribe hunting the bear, and one of them (represented by the star Mizar) has a cooking pot (the star Alcor) with him to cook the bear in once it is killed. The Arabs named these two as the "horse and rider," The ability to see this famous double star in the Plough is said to be a good test of your eyesight.

Many of the stars in Ursa Major are a similar distance from us, about 80 light-years. These stars are all moving in the same general direction. However, the two stars at each end of the Plough, Dubhe, and Alkaid move in a different direction.

Ursa Major has several deep-sky objects within its borders and seven "Messier" objects. In 1781 the French astronomer Charles Messier was a comet hunter. As part of his work, he catalogued anything in the night sky that could be mistaken for a comet. Ironically, although he achieved modest success as a comet hunter, discovering over 30, he is best known for this list known as the "Messier catalogue". This list includes many galaxies, nebulae, and clusters. Each of the Messier objects is prefaced with the letter M. For amateur astronomers, observing these objects is a real goal. Seeing all 110 Messier objects in one observing session in late spring is known as "doing the Messier marathon". At our latitude (54 degrees north), we cannot see them all in one night. To do so, you would need to head south to around about latitude 30 degrees north, to the Mediterranean, Canary Islands, Spain, or the southern United States.

Of the seven Messier objects within the borders of Ursa Major, two of them, the Pinwheel galaxy (M101) and Bodes' galaxy (M81), both being under 8th magnitude, are within reach of a small telescope.

A few years ago, I was on a cruise doing some stargazing on deck in the Mediterranean when a woman came up to me, and we started chatting. She asked if I could show her the pole star and the two bears in

The Plough (and aurora) from Iceland – 17th September 2019.

The Plough and aurora over Peel Castle – October 2015. *(Ron Strathdee)*

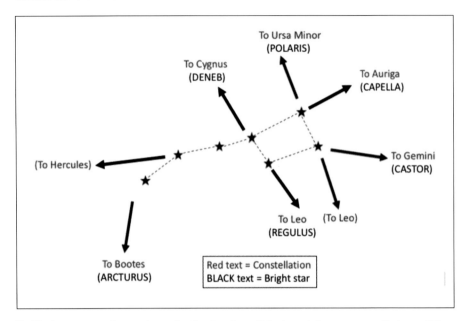

To Ursa Minor
(POLARIS)

To Cygnus
(DENEB)

To Auriga
(CAPELLA)

(To Hercules)

To Gemini
(CASTOR)

To Leo   (To Leo)
(REGULUS)

To Bootes
(ARCTURUS)

Red text = Constellation
BLACK text = Bright star

The Plough as a signpost.

the northern sky. I pointed out Polaris and the two constellations of Ursa Major, Ursa Minor. She became quite emotional and actually started to cry. She told me how her father had talked about seeing them before emigrating to Australia, but she had never seen them. It was, for both of us, a moving moment.

The Plough can, mainly due to its ease of identification, be used as a celestial signpost. Using these stars, it is possible to identify up to eight constellations and six bright stars.

Ursa Minor: The Little Bear
(Y Mucawin Befg)

Ursa Minor is always seen as a little bear, representing Arcas, the second of the two bears in the night sky. US astronomers usually refer to Ursa Minor as the "Little Dipper", but I prefer to see it as a "mini-Plough". Ursa Minor is another circumpolar constellation. We can use the brightest star in Ursa Minor, Polaris, in two distinct ways to help us navigate. Firstly, when you face Polaris, you are looking due north. Secondly, Polaris will always be at the same height above the northern horizon as the observer's latitude.

There is little else of significance in Ursa Minor. The two stars at the equivalent positions of the pointers in the Plough are Kocab and Pherkad Major. These are known as the "guardians of the pole". Kochab has a distinctive orange hue to it compared to the white Polaris.

Cassiopeia: The Queen

Cassiopeia represents the Queen who, along with her husband King Cepheus (who sits alongside his Queen in the heavens), ruled the ancient kingdom of Aethiopia. They are famous for their role in the legend of Andromeda. Cassiopeia comprises five bright stars and has a distinctive "W" shape in spring, whilst in autumn, when overhead, it looks like an "M". Some members of modern society see this as a celestial sign for the famous US burger chain,

Cassiopeia is very easily identified as all of the principal stars are bright, at magnitudes 2.2 to 3.3. Of the five, four are variable. The brightest is Shedir at magnitude 2.23, Chaph shines at magnitude 2.27, Cih at magnitude 2.2 can brighten on occasion to 1.6. Rucbah is at magnitude 2.68. Only Segin at magnitude 3.38 is not thought to be a variable star.

The constellation of Cassiopeia played an important part in the Copernican, or scientific revolution. In 1543, Nicolas Copernicus, the Polish astronomer, suggested that the Earth went around the Sun and not the other way around. This caused a considerable amount of controversy. Then, in 1572 a "new" star appeared in the constellation of Cassiopeia. The Danish astronomer Tycho Brahe observed this star, which we now

Cassiopeia: The Queen.

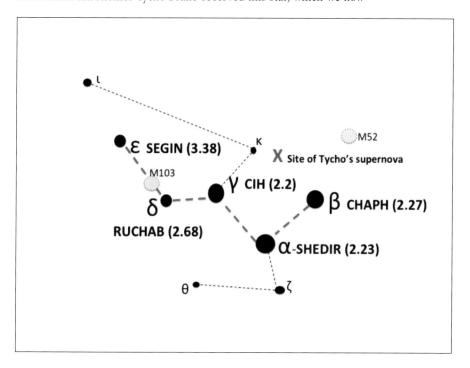

know was a supernova. His observations convinced him to put forward an alternative and complex theory to that of Copernicus. His work was so important and accurate that his assistant Johannes Kepler used these observations extensively. In 1609 he published two laws of planetary motion and a third in 1619. Newton used these laws in his deliberations, and in 1681 published his book "Principia", which confirmed that Copernicus's theory was correct.

Consequently, the appearance of Tycho's supernova in Cassiopeia in 1572 played a significant part in this scientific revolution. So, when you look at Cassiopeia for yourself in the northern skies, think about those important observations of this area of the sky all those years ago. These observations played such an essential part in the Copernican revolution and our understandings of the motions of the planets.

Cepheus: The King

Cepheus is a faint circumpolar constellation, also found by extending the line from the "pointers" in the Plough to Polaris a similar distance. Cepheus is adjacent to Cassiopeia. Both are the same size, but Cassiopeia is much brighter. Cepheus has only one star, Alderamin, brighter than magnitude 3.0. Cepheus was Cassiopeia's King and husband and the father of Andromeda.

The Garnet star, also known as Herschel's Garnet Star (Mu Cephei), has a distinctive red or garnet colour. It is one of the largest known stars with a radius of 1,000 times that of the Sun, and it is 100,000 times brighter than the Sun. It is the prototype of the Cepheid class of long-period variable stars. It varies erratically between magnitudes 3.4 and 5.1 over a period between 2.5 and 11 years.

Chapter 14

The Autumn Night Sky

In autumn, the progressively longer nights make astronomy especially rewarding. The long lighter summer nights are now behind us for another year. The Sun sets just before 8.00 PM. at the beginning of September and just before 4.00 PM. at the end of November.

In autumn, we have more or less finished with the bright stars of summer. The sky is now dominated by the faint but distinctive autumnal constellations in the southern sky. The autumn stars give us a sense of anticipation and a taste of what is to come over the coming months as we head towards winter with its bright stars and dramatic constellations. From November onwards, we start to get those cold, crisp nights when the stars and the night sky features are at their best. There is also the bonus of an extra hour in the evening after the clocks go back to Greenwich Mean Time (GMT) in late October. It always amuses me when people tell me that we get an extra hour of daylight after the clocks "fall back". The reality is that we just move this lost hour to the morning sky. Nothing has changed but the clock.

In early autumn, look towards the western horizon and about halfway

The Autumn sky.

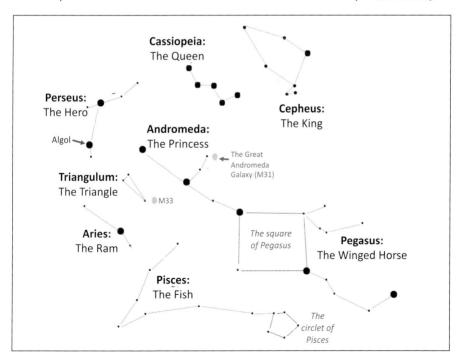

towards your zenith. You should still be able to see three bright stars from the summer, still clearly visible for a few more weeks. These three stars, Deneb, Vega, and Altair are the brightest in the constellations of Cygnus: The Swan, Lyra: The Lyre, and Aquila: The Eagle. Now look south, and the faint autumnal constellations will be visible. If you wait until around midnight, you will start to see the bright constellations of winter rising in the east. Another advantage of early autumn is that it does not usually get as cold as it does in mid-winter.-

There is an interesting observation that can be done in mid to late autumn. Find a place away from intrusive lights, and just look up at the night sky. Don't bother about trying to identify anything. Instead, just take in the view of the stars. It immediately becomes apparent that only a few bright stars are visible in the night sky in the south, compared to the other seasons.

The autumn night sky is dominated by the constellations, which contribute to the famous legend of Andromeda. To find the constellations of Cassiopeia: The Queen, Cepheus: The King, Perseus: The Hero, Andromeda: The Princess, Pegasus: The Winged Horse, and Cetus: The Whale, start by looking north. Find the star Polaris, the Pole Star, by using the pointer stars of the Plough. Follow this line up to the "W" or "M") shape of Cassiopeia. Then follow the right-hand "V" shape of the "W" in Cassiopeia down and to the right into the southern sky towards Pegasus. Before you get this far, you will find the constellation of Andromeda. Andromeda is made up of two faint converging lines of stars below Cassiopeia down to the top left of Pegasus. Pegasus represents a winged horse with a faint but distinctive asterism within it. The "Square of Pegasus" is a large square with very few stars inside it.

The Autumnal equinox

During September, as the length of daylight shrinks, the length of the night increases. The Sun heads southwards and will cross the Celestial Equator at a precise date and time between the 21st and 24th of September. This is defined as the autumnal equinox. A 21st September equinox is quite rare, but we will have two in the 21st century in 2092 and 2096. The last 24th September equinox took place in 1931. The date varies because of the insertion of leap years to correct the actual calendar to the Gregorian calendar.

There is a popular myth that day and night are precisely equal at the time of the equinox, but this is not the case. Atmospheric refraction affects the exact time. While this myth is correct at the equator, the actual date and time or "Equilux" can occur a few days earlier or later, depending on an observer's latitude.

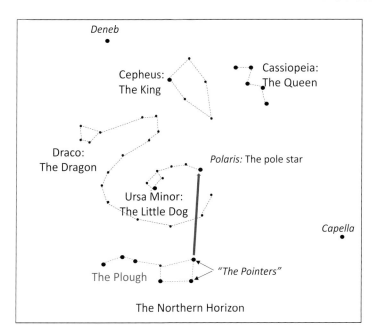

The Autumn circumpolar sky.

The northern sky in autumn

If you face the northern horizon, you will notice the well-known asterism of the Plough. It is sitting on the northern horizon. The pointer stars of Dubhe and Merak are pointing straight up to Polaris, the Pole star.

The Milky Way in autumn

Autumn is one of the best months of the year to see our galaxy, the Milky Way (*Raad Mooar Ree Gorree*), which can be seen clearly from our dark Manx skies. The Milky Way stretches right overhead from west to east at this time of year and seems to appear as if someone has thrown some milk across the sky. This is where the name comes from. The God Zeus let his infant son Heracles (whose mother was a mortal) suckle on his wife's (the Goddess Hera's) milk when she was asleep. When Hera awoke, she realised that she was breastfeeding an unknown infant. She pushed him away, and as a consequence, the milk was spilt from the babe's mouth. This is why the Milky Way looks like it does. In Latin, the Milky Way is known as "Via Lacteal", or the road of milk.

Andromeda legend

Regarded as one of mankind's oldest legends, the Andromeda legend illustrates mankind's assumed dominance over the animal kingdom. This theme is a significant part of the mythology of the 88 constellations in the skies.

In ancient times, Princess Andromeda was a mortal woman born to King Cepheus and Queen Cassiopeia of Aethiopia. Cassiopeia boasted that their daughter Andromeda was more beautiful than the sea nymphs, who were known for their astounding beauty. This arrogance angered Poseidon, the God of the sea, so he sent a monster to ravage the land as punishment. Cassiopeia and Cepheus begged for forgiveness. They were told that the monster's actions would only cease if they sacrificed their daughter. They were told to chain her to the rocks at the seashore, and she would be devoured by the monster. Cassiopeia and Cepheus did what was asked of them with great reluctance, and Andromeda was left to her fate. Fortunately, Perseus was flying home on his winged horse, Pegasus (although some versions say he was using his winged sandals). He noticed Andromeda chained to a rock awaiting her fate. He was captivated by her beauty and decided to rescue her. He had the Medusa's head in his bag, which he had just slain. Medusa's gaze would turn anyone looking at her into stone. Perseus had beheaded her by looking at her reflection in his polished shield. He pulled out the head, showed it to the monster Cetus. The monster looked into the eyes of Medusa and was turned to stone.

It had been previously arranged that Andromeda was to marry her uncle, Phineus, but Perseus had fallen in love with Andromeda the moment he saw her. So, after rescuing her, Perseus killed Phineus by employing Medusa's gaze once more. Perseus and Andromeda married and lived happily ever after. Upon her death, Andromeda was placed in the sky near the constellations of Cassiopeia, Cepheus, Perseus, Pegasus, and Cetus.

Andromeda: The Princess
(Yn Ven Gheulit)

Despite being the subject of the famous legend and containing one of the most beautiful features in our night sky, Andromeda is a faint constellation located in the autumn sky below and right of Cassiopeia. It has only three stars of the second magnitude.

The brightest star in Andromeda (Alperatz) is the top left star in the square of Pegasus and was formerly known as Beta Pegasi. Andromeda comprises a long linear shape of two converging lines. Thus, it can, with some imagination, be seen as a figure.

Opposite: The Autumn Milky Way from Langness, IOM – 21st October 2019. *(Ron Strathdee)*

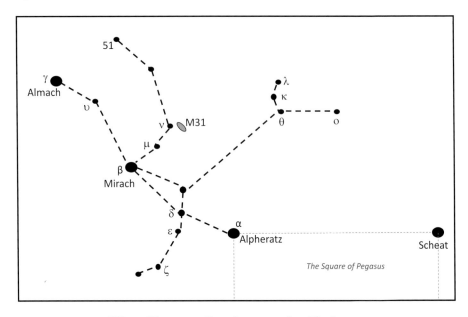

Andromeda: The
Princess.

The Great Andromeda Galaxy

Autumn is the best time of the year to find and see the Great Andromeda Galaxy (M31). This magnificent object can be seen on a dark moonless night from dark skies with good eyesight. It is at 3.7 magnitude, but the diffuse nature of the galaxy makes it appear fainter. How appropriate that one of the most beautiful objects in our night sky is within a constellation representing the beautiful Princess Andromeda.

The Great Andromeda Galaxy is famous for its appearance. It is also the object that led Edwin Hubble (whom the Hubble Space Telescope is named after) to realise that there are Galaxies other than our own Milky Way in the Universe. This discovery in 1922 led to an understanding that the Universe was much bigger than we had thought. This also led to what is now popularly known as the "Big Bang" theory

To find the Great Andromeda Galaxy, locate Alperatz, the upper right star of Pegasus's square, find the two stars to the upper left, and then go up two stars. The galaxy is just to the upper right of this second star. It will be visible with a pair of binoculars as a diffuse white/grey object. You may see it with the naked eye, but this depends on just how good your eyesight is. You are looking at an object 2.55 million light-years or 24,420,000,000,000,000,000 km away. It is a bit tedious writing all those zeros, so astronomers tend to use the "power of ten notation". We just put, as a superscript, the number of places that there needs to be after the decimal point. Andromeda is 2.4×10^{19} km (1.5×10^{19} miles) away. The Andromeda Galaxy is classified as being one

of what is termed "The Local Group". It is regarded as a near neighbour to our Milky Way. As a comparison, the Andromeda Galaxy is to the Milky Way as Onchan is to Douglas in the Isle of Man, if we regard the whole of the Earth as the Universe.

The Great Andromeda Galaxy (M31). *(Kevin Deakes)*

It used to be said that the Andromeda Galaxy was the furthest object visible to the naked eye, but it is now known that the nearby M33 Galaxy in the constellation of Triangulum is further away at 2.72 million light-years distant. Thus, M33 at magnitude 5.7 is just about visible to the naked eye from a dark sky location.

Pegasus: The Horse

The constellation of Pegasus represents the horse that Perseus rode after slaying the Medusa. Another version of the mythology of Pegasus is that it was the winged horse born from the body of the Medusa. Bellerophon, the son of Poseidon, rode the winged horse to the top of Mount Olympus after defeating the Chimaera. This act angered the God Zeus, who had Pegasus stung by an insect. The sting caused Bellerophon to fall to his death. Zeus then made Pegasus the carrier of his lightning bolts and honoured this role by placing him in the night sky.

Pegasus is quite large and features the asterism of the "great square of Pegasus". Pegasus is relatively easy to see in the night sky, but it looks very little like a horse. From our latitude in autumn, it seems to comprise a large square that dominates the southern sky. It includes three relatively bright

The Andromeda Galaxy, Point of Ayre, IOM
– 14th October 2018. *(Ron Strathdee)*

Andromeda Galaxy

The Stars of the Square of Pegasus showing the individual magnitudes.

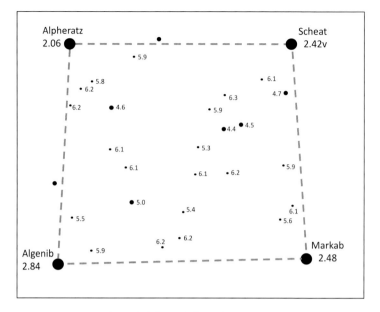

stars in Pegasus and one (Alpheratz) from the neighbouring constellation of Andromeda. It is relatively easy to see but is much larger than casual observers expect. Two stars of the summer triangle, Deneb and Vega in the west, can also be used to find Pegasus. Follow the line joining these two stars across the sky to the south, and you will see this large square above the southern horizon in mid-October at around 10:00 PM.

On a clear moonless night, try the "Pegasus Challenge". How many stars can you see inside the square with the naked eye? Assuming that the very faintest star you can see with the naked eye has a magnitude of 6.5, there are potentially 25 stars visible in the "Great Square of Pegasus". Spotting just one star within the square means you can see down to magnitude 4.4. There are four brighter than magnitude 5. A further ten stars are visible down to magnitude 6, and a further 11 stars between magnitude 6 and 6.5. In the nineteenth century, the German astronomer Johann Schmidt allegedly managed to count 102 stars within the square while working at his observatory in Athens. Schmidt must have had perfect eyesight, a great dark sky site, and great what we call "seeing" over in Greece all those years ago. In the Isle of Man, we have many dark sky locations, so when we get a good clear night, go outside and see how many you can see. I will permit the use of binoculars or a small telescope initially, but no cheating! It's only seeing them with the naked eye that counts!

Perseus: The Hero *(Yn Whing)*

Perseus has an indistinctive "K" or "M" shape and contains twelve stars brighter than the 4th magnitude. The brightest star is Mirphak at magnitude 1.8. The 2nd brightest star in Perseus is Algol, also known as the "demon star". Algol plays a significant role in the Andromeda legend. It adds an element of truth to it. Every 68 hours, Algol varies significantly in its brightness. Ancient observers concluded that this star represented the "winking eye of the demon", also known as the Medusa, whose gaze would turn anyone looking at her to stone.

Algol comprises two mutually rotating stars, a bright, primary star and a fainter, secondary star. When the fainter star passes in front of the primary star, the brightness drops. Then when the fainter star finishes passing in front of the primary star, the brightness returns to its previous level. The magnitude of Algol drops from 2.1 to 3.4 every 68.8 hours, and we can see this happen quite clearly and regularly with our naked eye in a dark night sky. However, it was not until 1782 that a satisfactory explanation was put forward for this variability. What is fascinating is that the ancient astronomers using just their naked eyes could discern differences in the brightness of Algol. Consequently, they used this information to deduce that it was a winking eye, and so the legend gained some credibility.

Perseus and the head of the Medusa at the Peterhof Palace, St Petersburg.

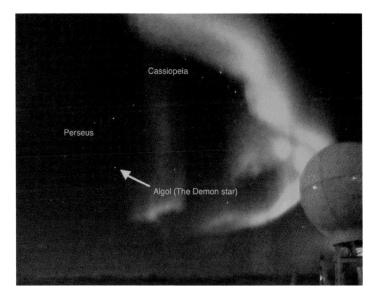

Cassiopeia, Perseus (and Algol) and Aurorae – Norway 17th March 2013.

Perseus has another notable feature within its borders: he points a sword towards Cassiopeia in his outstretched arm. Just to the right of the blade are two faint clusters of stars just visible to the naked eye. They are known as the "double cluster," or NGC 869 and NGC 884. (NGC stands for New General Catalogue, another catalogue of deep-sky features compiled in 1888). This is also near the location of the Perseid meteor shower radiant.

Pisces: The Fish *(Ny Eeastyn)*

The zodiacal constellation of Pisces is located below Pegasus. Whilst Pisces looks nothing like a fish, it has a great legend. To escape from the fire-breathing Typhon, mother and son (Aphrodite and Eros) turned themselves into fish and jumped into the Euphrates. To ensure they did not lose each other, they tied their tails together. This is marked by the star Al Rishna, which translated from Arabic means "the knot".

Pisces is a faint constellation, the fourth largest of the twelve signs of the zodiac, but there are only three stars brighter than the fourth magnitude in Pisces. It does have a faint but distinctive asterism comprising a "circlet" of stars which is an excellent test for "seeing" on clear autumn nights. The spring or vernal equinox, where the ecliptic crosses the celestial equator, is actually within the constellation of Pisces, just below and left of the circlet.

Fomalhaut

Using the right-hand edge of the square of Pegasus, follow this line down, and you will find a solitary bright star, relatively low near the south-eastern horizon. This star, Fomalhaut is the brightest star in the constellation Pisces Australis (the Southern Fish). The declination of Fomalhaut is -29 degrees. This means the highest it can get above our horizon is just 7 degrees. Fomalhaut, at magnitude 1.16, is the 18th brightest star in the night skies. In 2008 Fomalhaut was one of the first stars thought to have a planetary system. A Hubble Space telescope picture of Fomalhaut was taken with the star's light hidden or "occulted". This enabled astronomers to see what it was thought were "Extra-Solar planets". One of these was named Dagon or Fomalhaut b. However, in 2020, new observations from the Hubble Space Telescope show that Fomalhaut b is probably just an expanding dust cloud.

Fomalhaut does have another claim to fame. It was one of the navigational stars used by the Apollo 13 astronauts to help them get home, following an explosion in the spacecraft's service module, which nearly led to the loss of the crew in April 1970.

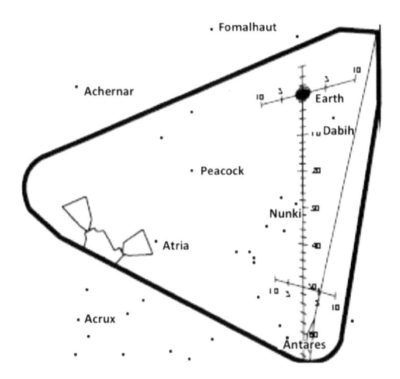

The navigational stars in the window from Apollo 13 lunar module.

Meteor showers visible in the autumn sky

There are three showers visible in the autumn months. First, the Orionids may be seen between 2nd October and 7th November, peaking on 21st October. Second, the Taurids may be seen between 20th September and 10th December, peaking around 12th November. Finally, the Leonids may be seen between 6th and 13th November, peaking around the 17th.

Chapter 15

The Winter Night Sky

Winter starts with the faint autumnal constellations of Pegasus, Andromeda, and Pisces setting earlier and earlier each night. But the most casual sky-watcher can't fail to notice in late autumn, rising in the east, a large number of bright stars. These are the stars of the winter constellations, Taurus: The Bull, Orion: The Hunter, Gemini: The Twins, and the two dog constellations of Canis Major and Canis Minor. We also have three potentially good meteor showers to observe during the winter months.

We are very fortunate in the Isle of Man because we have excellent dark skies. We see these wonderful constellations throughout our dark winter evenings in the northern hemisphere. Spare a thought for our friends down under, who only get to see Orion and his entourage in their summer skies. During our winter, the night sky takes on a spectacular beauty all of its own when we have those cold frosty nights, and the atmosphere can be very clear. This is because the clarity of the sky, or "seeing", is much better when there is lower humidity.

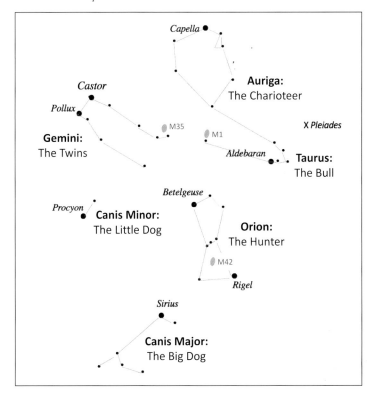

The Winter sky –
Looking south.

The northern sky in winter

Of the thirty brightest stars visible in the night sky, twenty-one of these can be seen from our shores. Twelve of these are visible in our winter skies, three in spring, five in summer, and just the one in autumn. This is why we believe that the northern winter sky is the best of the year for stargazing. The reality is that there are simply a more significant number of brighter stars in this area of the sky, regardless of when and where you are viewing them. When you go outside, look in all directions but ignore the east initially. Only after viewing in all the other directions, look east. The number of very bright stars visible in this part of the sky is quite a contrast.

The first of the winter constellations to appear in our skies is Taurus: The Bull. The first part of Taurus that rises in our eastern sky is a group of stars known as the Pleiades *(Y Trilleen)*. They are also known as the Seven Sisters. The group looks like a fuzzy patch in the sky to the naked eye. However, a pair of binoculars shows them as a tightly knit group of many stars, seven of which are brighter than the others.

Following the stars of Taurus into the winter sky are the bright stars of the constellation Orion: The Hunter. Orion is one of the most spectacular constellations in the whole night sky. There are three bright stars within Orion in a line sloping up from left to right. These three stars are known as Orion's belt. Following the belt upwards to the right, you will come to the star Aldebaran in Taurus. If you follow this line further upwards, you come to the Pleiades star cluster.

The Winter stars over Snuff the Wind Mine, Foxdale IOM – 28th February 2021. *(Ron Strathdee)*

Now go back to Orion's belt, but this time follow the line down to the left. It will lead to a very bright star: Sirius, the brightest star in the night sky. Sirius is often called the "Dog Star" because it is the principal star of the constellation of Canis Major: The Great Dog. Canis Major is one of two dogs in the sky in this part of the sky, the other being Canis Minor: The Little Dog, which is above Sirius and left of Orion.

Winter Solstice

The winter solstice usually occurs in the northern hemisphere on either 21st or 22nd December. This is when the Sun reaches its lowest point above the southern horizon. Consequently, we get the least hours of daylight. Exceptionally, the winter solstice can occur as early as 20th December (2080) or as late as 23rd December (1903 and 2303). After the winter solstice, we can forward to the lighter nights of spring and summer.

At the time of the winter solstice at noon from the latitude of the Isle of Man, the maximum altitude of our Sun will only be 12.5 degrees. However, at noon at the summer solstice, the Sun will be 59.5 degrees above the southern horizon. The difference of 47 degrees is twice the axial tilt (23.5 x 2). We can measure this for ourselves using the upright fist extended at arm's length, which is approximately 10 degrees.

If you face the northern horizon, you will notice that the asterism of the Plough is now on the right of the NCP and is standing on its tail or handle. The pointer stars of Dubhe and Merak are now level with or higher than Polaris.

The changing altitude of the Sun at the time of the solstices.

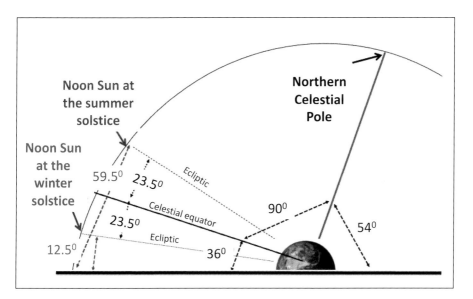

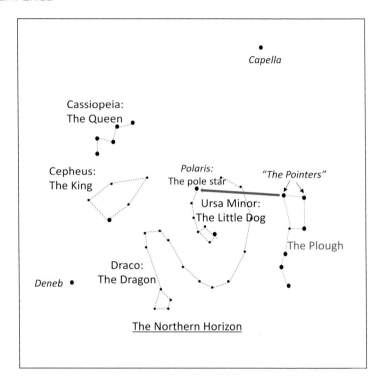

The Milky Way in winter

Although not as dramatic as autumn, the Milky Way is still visible in our winter sky. It stretches right across the sky from the north-western to the south-eastern horizon. However, if you want to see it make sure your eyes are used to the dark, it can take about 15 minutes to get fully dark-adapted, and then the Milky Way will be seen as a faint cloud stretching across the sky. The other thing you need to watch out for is that when the Moon is approaching full, the Milky Way is practically invisible. The Moon is one of the most significant sources of light pollution around, so always look for the Milky Way a week before or after the New Moon.

Taurus: The Bull *(Y Tarroo)*

The constellation of Taurus is one of the zodiacal constellations. According to Greek mythology, Taurus represents the God Zeus, who changed himself into a white bull to win the heart of Europa, the Phoenician princess. After winning her affection, she climbed onto his back, and he swam back to Crete across the Mediterranean with her. Taurus always heralds the onset of winter with its jewel, the Pleiades star cluster, becoming apparent in the eastern sky as early as mid-October.

The Pleiades (M45) or seven sisters is an open cluster of stars representing Atlas's seven daughters. After Atlas was forced to carry the heavens on his shoulders, Zeus, the ruler of the Greek Gods, transformed the daughters, first into doves and then into stars. The nearby constellation of Orion still pursues them across the night sky. According to some versions of the myth, all seven sisters committed suicide as they were saddened by the loss of their sibling, Hyades (another cluster in Taurus). Consequently, Zeus immortalised the sisters by placing them in the sky, and these seven stars formed the star cluster of the Pleiades.

The annual (or heliacal) rising of the Pleiades coincides with the yearly flooding of the Nile, which was so important all those years ago. This yearly flooding was thought to have been caused by the weeping of the sisters. A more recent interpretation is from the car manufacturer Subaru. They have a badge on the front of all their cars, representing the Pleiades, but it only shows 6 stars. The missing seventh star is the car!

The brightest star in Taurus is Aldebaran, which is known as the "eye of the bull". Aldebaran is a red supergiant star, shining at magnitude 0.86. It is the 14th brightest star in the night sky and has a notable reddish hue to it. Aldebaran sits within another open cluster of about 200 stars, the Hyades.

The badge on a Subaru car.

The rising Winter stars from Bradda Head – 15th March 2016. *(Ron Strathdee)*

Pleiades

Astronomically, this cluster is relatively close to us, at just 153 light-years distant. Aldebaran appears to be within the group but is actually only half the distance away at 72 light-years distance.

Finally, in Taurus, we also have an object that has been of great significance in astronomy for many years. The Messier object, M1, is a remnant from a star that exploded as a supernova seen by Chinese astronomers back in 1054. In 1967 it was realised that the supernova remnant was spinning rapidly, and a new type of pulsing star or "Pulsar" was discovered.

Orion: The Hunter *(Y Shelgeyr Mooar)*

Orion is probably the most well-known and spectacular constellation in the entire night sky. This is because Orion straddles the celestial equator. Meaning that it is visible from anywhere on the Earth, depending on the season.

Orion represents the greatest hunter who ever lived. He fell in love with Merope, the daughter of the King of Chios, Oenopion. He was forbidden to marry Merope unless all the beasts in the woods were slain. Orion and Merope planned to elope, but Oenopion blinded him. His sight was eventually restored by Helios (the Sun God), and he then fell in love with

Orion: The Hunter.

Aurora. Orion was, however, killed by a scorpion and was placed in the night sky opposite Scorpio for all eternity.

Orion has a distinctive belt of three stars. Hanging from this belt is his sword, home to the great Orion nebulae, a stellar nursery. The Orion Nebula (M42) is an enormous cloud of gas and dust. It is 1,300 light-years away and is about 30 to 40 light-years in diameter. In 2012, it was suggested the Orion Nebula could have a black hole at its centre. The four brightest stars in the Orion Nebula can be seen through modest-sized telescopes and are known as "The Trapezium". The light of these young, hot stars illuminates the Orion Nebula. These stars are only a million or so years old, just babies in cosmic terms.

Using Orion as a celestial signpost

Orion is another constellation (the other being Ursa Major) used as a celestial signpost.

Using just two or three stars in Orion, you can find eight other constellations and four of the 30 brightest stars. Orion itself comprises seven bright stars, another four of which also feature in this list. All seven of Orion's brightest stars feature in a list of the top 75 brightest stars.

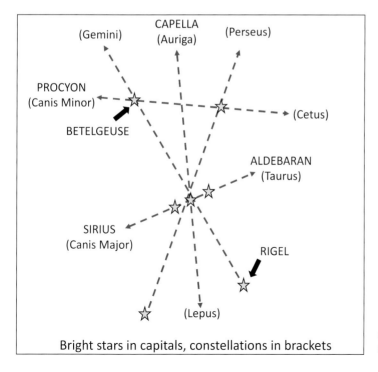

Bright stars in capitals, constellations in brackets

Orion as a celestial signpost.

Betelgeuse

The top left star in Orion is the distinctly red coloured Betelgeuse. Betelgeuse is thought to be about 640 light-years away. Betelgeuse is massive. Its diameter would extend beyond the orbit of Jupiter if it were placed in the Sun's position in our solar system. It shines red because it is a huge star, heading towards the end of its life. We believe that Betelgeuse will explode as a supernova sometime soon, probably within the next million years. Exactly when it is difficult to predict. It depends on precise calculations of its mass and a greater understanding of the processes inside the star.

In late 2019 and early 2020, it was noticed that Betelgeuse was fading far more than was usually expected. Betelgeuse normally shines at magnitude + 0.5 (10th brightest star in the night sky) and can drop to a magnitude of about +0.9. By February 2020, it had fallen to +1.70 magnitude), making Betelgeuse just the 30th brightest star. Some astronomers speculated that Betelgeuse was about to explode as a supernova. However, Hubble Space Telescope observations have shown that the unexpected dimming of Betelgeuse was most likely caused by an immense amount of material being ejected into space. This formed a dust cloud that blocked the starlight coming from Betelgeuse's surface.

The Belt of Orion

The three stars of Orion's Belt are one of the most distinctive asterisms of the night sky. All three are bright, and nowhere else in the night sky are three bright stars in a line as close as these three. They comprise the stars from left to right, Alnitak (magnitude 1.77), Alnilam (1.69), and Mintaka (2.20). When showing a group, the wonders of the winter night sky, I often ask them to tell me the order of brightness of the three. Without fail, everyone recognises Mintaka as being the faintest. Try it for yourself.

Another exercise to try is to see how many stars you can see with the naked eye within the rectangle of Orion bound by Betelgeuse, Bellatrix, Rigel and Saiph. This is often used to assess light pollution in the night sky from a particular location. If you can see 25 to 30 or more, you will be observing from a dark location. If, however, you can only see about 10, then you have heavily polluted night skies. I have often done this exercise with my UCM astronomy students and IOMAS members. I have seen over 30 stars on several occasions. We deduce that we have excellent dark skies in many parts of the Isle of Man.

Rigel

The brightest star in Orion, at the bottom right, is Rigel. At magnitude 0.10, Rigel is the seventh brightest star in the night sky. Rigel is about 860 light-years distant and is a blue-white supergiant star estimated to be anywhere from 120,000 to 279,000 times as luminous as the Sun. Rigel is also an important navigational star. It is bright, easily located and equatorially, and thus visible worldwide.

Another interesting feature of Orion is that it is home to the Orionid meteor shower, which occurs on and around the 15th of October each year.

Gemini: The Twins *(My Lannoonyn)*

As Orion is still rising on a winter's evening, you may notice above left of Orion two bright stars, one above the other. These are the two brightest stars of the zodiacal constellation of Gemini: The Twins. The uppermost star in Gemini is Castor at magnitude 1.62, the 24th brightest star in the night sky. Castor is above and to the right of Pollux at magnitude 1.14, the 17th brightest. The two are 52 and 34 light-years away, respectively. Pollux is half a magnitude brighter than its twin. It is also notably yellow/orange in colour compared to the blue/white of Castor. Castor is the closest of the two to Polaris, the Pole star. Thus, it is sometimes described as the "castor" upon which the heavens revolve. The vernal equinox was in Gemini in 4,500 BC.

This area of the sky has been associated with two people or twins throughout history. The ancient Chinese saw them as Yin and Yang, the Romans as Romulus and Remus, the founders of Rome. In Greek mythology, Castor and Pollux were twin half-brothers, both sons of Queen Leda of Sparta. Castor was the mortal son, whose father was King Tyndareus of Sparta, whilst Pollux was immortal, the son of the God Zeus. Both were members of Jason's crew on the Argo Navis searching for the Golden Fleece. When Castor died, Pollux pleaded that he should share his immortality, and both were placed side and side by Zeus in the sky for eternity.

Gemini contains the open cluster M35, visible to the naked eye at magnitude 5.0 under dark skies. It is 2,750 light-years away. Gemini is home to one of the year's best meteor showers: the Geminids. The shower radiates every December, peaking on around 12th December, from a point near Castor's feet.

Auriga: The Charioteer *(Yn Fainagh)*

Above Gemini is a distinctive five-sided shape of stars, representing the constellation of Auriga: The Charioteer. Auriga's brightest star is the yellow-hued star, Capella. At magnitude 0.08, Capella is the sixth brightest star in the night sky and, in winter, is almost directly overhead. Mythologically

Auriga represents the lame goat herder Erichthonius. He invented the chariot and, as a consequence, was immortalised by the Gods who placed him in the sky for eternity. Auriga has a distinctive pentagon shape and shares one of its stars with the nearby zodiacal constellation of Taurus. There is also a faint but distinctive triangle, called "the kids", representing three goats. Look for yourself and see if you can see Erichthonius riding his chariot across the sky with three goats under his arm.

The bright Capella is 42 light-years distant and is much bigger than the Sun. It has a similar spectral type to our Sun and is always seen as having a slightly yellowish tinge. This compares well with the nearby reddish coloured stars of Aldebaran and Betelgeuse in the constellations of Taurus and Orion, respectively.

Canis Major: The Big Dog

Canis Major is one of two dog constellations in this part of the sky, the other being Canis Minor. Both dogs are connected to the myth of the Teumessian Fox that were turned to stone and placed in the skies by Zeus to accompany Orion. Interestingly both dogs have always been seen as two separate breeds. Canis Major is easy to locate by following Orion's belt, down to the left, which leads to the brightest star in the night sky Sirius. Sirius, at magnitude -1.4, is one of the nearest stars to us, only eight light-years away. Like Rigel, it shines predominantly bluey/white, but Sirius also appears to twinkle and change colour dramatically. Sirius is also known as the Dog Star. The second brightest star in Canis Major, at magnitude 1.50, Adhara, is the 22nd brightest in our night sky. VY Canis Major is one of the largest and most one of the largest and most luminous stars in our galaxy. Canis Major is also home to M41, an open cluster 2,300 light-years away and visible to the naked eye at magnitude 4.5.

Canis Minor: The Little Dog

Canis Minor is a small constellation representing the smaller of Orion's dogs, both placed in the sky by Zeus. Canis Major has just two named stars within its borders. Procyon, the eighth brightest star in our night sky at magnitude 0.34, and Gomeisa at 2.9 magnitude. Procyon has a slight orange colour that is quite noticeable compared to Sirius. At just 11 light-years distance, Procyon is one of the nearest bright stars to the Earth.

Winter Hexagon

Astronomers in the northern hemisphere always regard winter as the best time of the year to look at the stars. There are twelve bright stars visible in the southern sky, as seen in our skies in January at around 10.00 PM. All twelve of these stars feature in the top 30 brightest stars, as detailed in Table 2 (page 143). The large number of bright stars in this area allows us to link six of them into an asterism we call the "winter hexagon".

To locate the winter hexagon for yourself, start with Sirius in Canis Major, close to the southern horizon, at about 10.00 PM. To the left and up from Sirius is the star Procyon in Canis Minor. Next in our hexagon is the star Castor, in Gemini, above and slightly to the left of Procyon. Castor is above and to the right of Pollux, which is not generally included in the winter hexagon. Next, up and left almost overhead, is the star Capella in Auriga. Now move down and to the left to Aldebaran, in the constellation of Taurus. Finally, in the perimeter of our hexagon, come down and to the right to the star Rigel in Orion. However, the jewel in the winter hexagon lies near its centre. Betelgeuse, even redder in colour than Aldebaran.

The winter hexagon always surprises observers because of its size. It stretches from near the horizon from Sirius to Capella, almost overhead. If you then place Betelgeuse in the centre of the hexagon. Add in the stars Pollux in Gemini, El Nath in Taurus, Bellatrix, and Alnilam from Orion's belt. Another bright star Adhara in Canis Major, is just outside the

The Winter Hexagon.

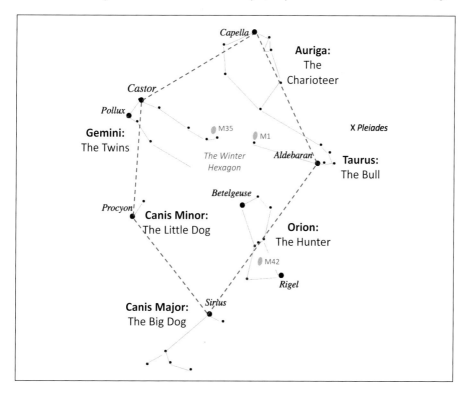

hexagon. This is by far the largest concentration of bright stars anywhere in the night sky. On cold clear winter's evening, look southwards at around 10.00 PM. Look for yourself and wonder at the spectacle of these twelve celestial superstars.

Another well-known asterism in the winter sky is the "Winter Triangle". This comprises the stars Procyon in Canis Minor, Betelgeuse in Orion, and Sirius in Canis Major.

The Scotty dog asterism

From our home, we can clearly see the southern sky. On numerous occasions, my wife Sandra would tell me in the late autumn/early winter that she could see what she called the "Scotty dog". Knowing that the constellations Canis Minor and Canis Major are in this area of sky, I assumed that this is what she saw. However, one night whilst we were out, Sandra mentioned it again, and I asked her to show me exactly where she was looking. She pointed to the belt of Orion and the area below and to the right of it. My interest was piqued. I pressed her for more details and learnt that she was looking at a distinctive asterism. This comprised Rigel and the stars of Orion's belt, Orion's sword, and the star Cursa in the constellation Eridanus.

What amazes me is that two dogs have been seen in this area for centuries. Now, independently of any astronomical knowledge, Sandra had seen and identified another dog in this area of the sky!

Meteor showers visible in the winter sky

The Geminid meteor shower peaks from 10th to 13th December and is always a reliable meteor source. Another meteor shower, the Ursids, peaks around 24th December. This shower radiates from the constellation of Ursa Major near the northern horizon. Finally, often forgotten, the Quadrantid meteor shower from the same general area peaks on and around the 2nd to 5th January. This shower is named after the defunct constellation of Quadrans Muralis. Defunct, because in 1930, the International Astronomical Union (IAU) consolidated the number of constellations from hundreds to a more realistic 88. The radiant is also close to Ursa Major, but the shower is often overlooked given the time of year. Meteor spotters usually avoid looking whilst the Moon is between the first and third quarter. However, with the Ursids and Quadrantids radiant's being in the northern sky, it is worth looking at regardless of the Moon's phase.

So, on a clear January night, take yourself outside and look towards the southern horizon. Just marvel at the majesty of the winter skies, the magnificent Orion, and the winter hexagon, the winter triangle, and don't forget the Scotty Dog, all of which dominate the winter night sky.

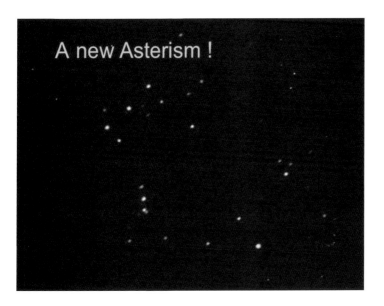

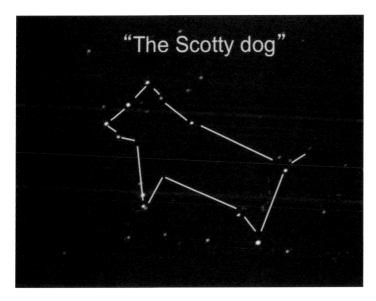

The Asterism of the "Scotty dog".

Chapter 16

The Spring Night Sky

Opposite: The Milky Way in Spring from Langness, IOM – 27th May 2017. *(Ron Strathdee)*

Spring is always a good time for stargazing. Unlike the cold frosty nights of winter, it can be warmer. However, despite the hour going back in March, the Sun still sets quite early, so we still get the opportunity to see a dark sky from about 9.00 PM. onwards. The spring sky does not have as many bright stars as the winter. There are just three compared to twelve. But most of the winter stars are still visible in the western sky after sunset. The constellations of Orion, Taurus, Canis Major, and Canis Minor are rapidly disappearing into the twilight sky, leaving just the constellation of Gemini visible throughout April and early May. Look towards the north-eastern horizon, and you will see that the Plough is almost overhead. Follow the curve of the handle of the Plough down towards the eastern horizon to a bright star, Arcturus, the brightest star in the constellation of Bootes, The Herdsman. Follow this curve further down and right towards the horizon to the bright star, Spica, the brightest star in the constellation Virgo: The Virgin. To the right and up from Spica is another bright star Regulus, the brightest star in the constellation of Leo: The Lion.

These three stars, Arcturus (magnitude -0.05), Spica (magnitude 0.97), and Regulus (magnitude 1.39), are the 4th, 16th, and 21st brightest, respectively. The three constellations of Leo, Virgo (both signs of the zodiac), and Bootes are easily found near the north-eastern horizon in early spring evenings.

The spring night sky – looking south.

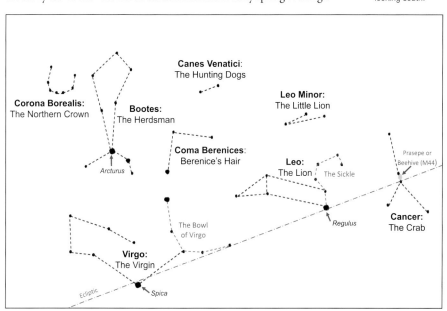

The vernal equinox *(Cormid traa-arree)*

The vernal (or spring) equinox in the northern hemisphere is defined as when the Sun crosses the celestial equator heading northwards, and the Earth's geographical poles are upright. The vernal equinox is generally on 20th March but can vary by one day either way. The last time the March equinox was on 19th March was in 1999. The next is in 2044. The previous 21st March equinox was in 2007, the next is in 2101.

It is the vernal equinox that determines the date of Easter. Easter Sunday is always the following Sunday after the Full Moon after the vernal equinox. This means that Easter Sunday can be as early as 22nd March (2285) or as late as 25th April (2038).

The location on the celestial sphere where the Sun crosses the celestial equator northwards is called the "first point of Aries". However, this point is no longer in the constellation of Aries: The Ram *(Y Rea)* but is in the constellation of Pisces. This is due to a wobble in the Earth's axis (known as "precession"). This causes the first point of Aries to travel westwards across the sky at a rate of roughly one degree every 72 years. Based on the modern constellation boundaries, the vernal equinox passed from Gemini into Taurus in 4000 BC, then passed into Aries in 1866 BC and into Pisces in 68 BC. It will pass into Aquarius: The Water Carrier *(Yn Ymmyrkagh Ushtey)* in 2597 AD and into Capricorn in 4312 AD.

Even though the vernal equinox will not be in Aquarius for over 500 years, in popular culture, the expression "Age of Aquarius" usually refers to the heyday of the hippie and new age movements of the 1960s and 1970s. The successful 1967 Broadway musical "Hair" with its opening song "Aquarius" and the memorable line *"this is the dawning of the Age of Aquarius"* brought an awareness of the Aquarian age concept to the attention of a worldwide audience. The 1969 Woodstock festival was advertised as "An Aquarian Exposition". In December 2020, the closest planetary conjunction of Jupiter and Saturn since 1623 occurred. Some of the media described this as being in the constellation of Aquarius, but the actual conjunction took place in the adjacent constellation of Capricorn.

The northern sky in spring

If you face the northern horizon, you will notice that the Plough asterism is now almost overhead. This is because the pointer stars of Dubhe and Merak are high in the sky and point almost directly downwards to Polaris, the Pole star.

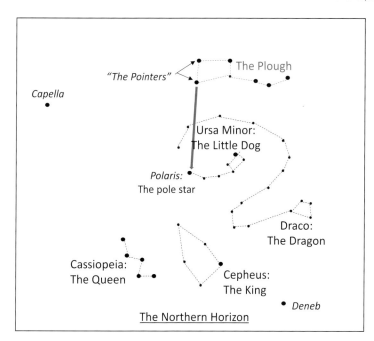

The Plough

"The Pointers"

Capella

Ursa Minor:
The Little Dog

Polaris:
The pole star

Draco:
The Dragon

Cassiopeia:
The Queen

Cepheus:
The King

Deneb

The Northern Horizon

The Spring
circumpolar sky.

The Milky Way in spring

In spring, the Milky Way sits just above the horizon from the north-eastern sky to the south-western sky and is less noticeable. This is because it crosses the sky at a much shallower angle than at other times of the year. We are also looking away from the galactic centre at this time of year, so we do not see the rich star clouds and dust lanes we see in late summer.

Leo: The Lion *(Y Lion)*

Leo is a zodiacal constellation and one of the few constellations that looks a bit like what it is meant to represent and is relatively easy to interpret as a lion. Leo represents the Nemean lion that Hercules had to slay as the first of his twelve labours. There are six Messier objects in Leo. All are galaxies located at about 35 million light-years away.

Leo's brightest star is Regulus, the "dot" in a reversed question mark. Regulus is also known as the "King" or "Royal" star and is located near the lion's heart. To the east (or left) of Leo is the constellation Virgo, with its bright star Spica. Regulus is very close to the ecliptic and can be occulted by the Moon or on rare occasions, by

Leo: The Lion, one of the few constellations that looks a little what it represents.

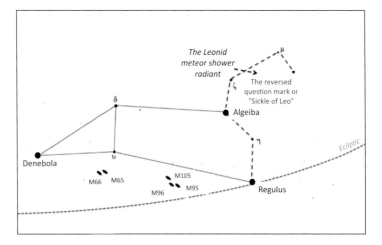

Venus. In 1959 Venus occulted Regulus. Such an event will occur again on 1st. October 2044.

Cancer: The Crab *(Y Paryan)*

The faint zodiacal constellation of Cancer sits between the much brighter constellations of Gemini and Leo. It represents the crab that was sent to harass Hercules during his labours. The crab was accidentally killed when stood upon but was rewarded with a place in the heavens for its efforts.

Cancer is quite tricky to see and only has two stars within it brighter than the fourth magnitude. The brightest star, Altarf, has a magnitude of 3.6, and Asellus Australis is at magnitude 3.9. So, unless you observe on a moonless night from a dark location, Cancer is challenging to make out.

The impressive open cluster (M44) known as the Beehive or Praesepe, from the Latin word for "manger". The Beehive lies at the centre of Cancer. Using a pair of binoculars or a small telescope as a guide, you can just about see this faint object with the naked eye. Many of these open clusters are visible in the night sky, and the Beehive is one of the closest to Earth at just under 600 light-years distant.

Virgo: The Virgin *(Y Voidyn)*

Mythologically, Virgo is associated with Astraea, the Goddess of innocence and purity. When Zeus sent Pandora down to the Earth, Pandora opened a box she had been told to leave untouched and released various plagues. Subsequently, the Gods all returned to the heavens, and Astraea was the last to leave Earth. Virgo is usually depicted with angel-like wings.

Virgo is one of the twelve zodiac constellations and is the second-largest constellation in the sky (after Hydra). The Sun passes through Virgo at the time of the harvest. The star Spica is a blue supergiant and one of the nearest massive binary stars *(Rollage Ghoobie)*. It is 260 light-years away. Virgo can be seen as a letter "Y" with Spica at the bottom. We can use this shape to find the asterism of the "bowl of Virgo," filled with the Virgo cluster, an area rich in galaxies, all about 13 million light-years away. When observing this sky area, we are looking out beyond our Milky Way.

Coma Berenices: Queen Berenice's Hair

Just above Virgo is the small faint constellation of Coma Berenices or Coma, as it is usually abbreviated. Coma is home to the Coma cluster, another area of the night sky rich in galaxies. The whole area is worth looking at with a pair of binoculars or a small telescope.

The mythology of the Coma has a hint of truth. King Ptolemy had waged a long war with the Assyrians. When he returned victorious from the war, his wife Berenice, as a tribute, had her beautiful hair ceremoniously clipped and laid out on the altar. The following morning the hair was missing. The King was furious and hinted that the priests might be sacrificed if the hair could not be found. It was the court astronomer Conon of Samos who came to their rescue. He advised that the Goddess Aphrodite had accepted the gift of Berenice's hair. This had been placed in the heavens next to Leo for all eternity to celebrate Ptolemy's triumph. On a dark moonless night, find the bright star Spica for yourself and then look above it above the "Y" shape of the bowl of Virgo. You may see a faint shimmering feature above this bowl, which appears slightly like hair. These galaxies of the Coma cluster are 330 million light-years away.

Bootes: The Herdsman *(Y Bochilley)*

There are several myths about the constellation of Bootes: The Herdsman. One of the most popular is that he represents the Herdsman who invented the Plough. The 4th brightest star in the sky, Arcturus, is in Bootes. Arcturus has a distinctive orangey-white colour and can easily be found by following the curve of the handle of the Plough downwards at the base of a kite or ice cream cone-shaped constellation.

In 1933 the US city of Chicago wanted something exceptional and innovative to mark its "Century of Progress Exposition". It was looking for a way to indicate just how far the city had come since its establishment 100 years earlier. The organisers wanted to pay tribute to the previous "World Columbian Exposition" This was held in Chicago in 1893 to commemorate

Christopher Columbus's arrival in America some 400 years earlier in 1492. A unique idea was born to light up the 1933 Expo site using a light beam that left a star in 1893. Astronomers at the time estimated that Arcturus was located 40 light-years from Earth. The light emitted from Arcturus during the World's Columbian Exposition in 1893 would reach the Earth in 1933, in time for the opening of the 1933 Expo.

So, at 9:15 PM. on 27th May 1933, four telescopes located in different observatories in the region captured the light from Arcturus and activated a circuit at the Exposition site and lit up the floodlights before a crowd of 30,000. Thus, in 1933, Arcturus was one of the most famous stars in the cosmos and made the front page of every newspaper in the United States. Even today, what they achieved is seen as a "shining" example of the technological progress of the time. Although we now believe that Arcturus is a little nearer at 37 light-years away.

On 31st October each year in the Isle of Man, we celebrate "Hop Tu Naa," often described as the Manx equivalent of Halloween. Arcturus rises at the same place in the east and sets at the same time and place in the west that the summer Sun did three months earlier. That's why, every year at this time, you can consider the star Arcturus to be the *"Ghost of the summer Sun"*.

Meteor showers visible in the spring sky

The Lyrid meteor shower peaks between the 18th to 25th of April. Look out for meteors appearing to come from the north-eastern sky around midnight. On a moonless night, you should get to see up to about 10 to 15 meteors per hour from a dark location.

Chapter 17

The Summer Night Sky

The long, light, but hopefully warm nights of summer mean that we don't get many chances to do much astronomy because it does not get dark enough. But we can still see some great constellations, a few bright stars, and one of the best meteor showers of the year. Between the end of May and early August, anywhere of latitude of around 54 degrees north officially does not get beyond "astronomical twilight". Consequently, we cannot see any faint objects or dark skies during this period. It is not officially "night-time" or dark until the Sun gets below 18 degrees below the horizon. Astronomical twilight is defined as when the Sun is between 12 and 18 degrees below our horizon. Once we get beyond astronomical twilight in mid to late August,

Summer sky looking south.

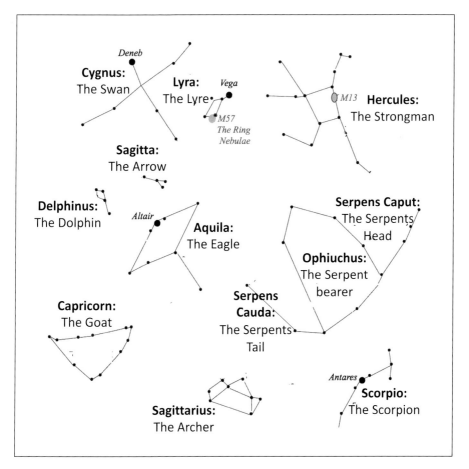

we start to enjoy a lengthening period of darkness as we head towards the autumnal equinox and the winter solstice.

In the lighter nights of summer, the three bright stars of spring, Regulus, Spica, and Arcturus, follow each other, setting in the western sky. The summer constellations of Cygnus: The Swan, Lyra: The Lyre, Aquila: The Eagle and Hercules: The Strongman will be high in the sky with the zodiacal constellations of Libra: The Scales *(Ny Meihaghyn)*, Scorpio: The Scorpion and Sagittarius: The Archer just visible above the southern horizon. Whilst difficult to see, Scorpio is worth the effort as it contains the distinctively red coloured star Antares, one of the largest stars in the sky. Just above Sagittarius and left of Scorpio are the constellations of Ophiuchus: The Serpent Bearer and Serpens: The Snake. Serpens is unique in the 88 constellations as it is in two parts, the head (Caput) and tail (Cauda). Ophiuchus holds the two parts in his hands. Whether the snake is in two distinct parts or if the two are linked behind Ophiuchus is a matter of conjecture. All three are very faint. The brightest star in Ophiuchus is Rasalhague at magnitude 2.08.

The Summer Solstice

The summer solstice, or more correctly the June solstice, is defined as when the Sun reaches its highest altitude above the southern horizon. The maximum altitude of the Sun at noon at the time of the June solstice is 59½ degrees. Whilst at the December solstice, the Sun's maximum altitude is just 12½ degrees above the horizon. This seasonal variation is due to the Earth's axial tilt of 23½ degrees. The June solstice can occur between 20th and 22nd June. However, a 22nd June solstice is quite rare: the last was in 1975, and the next won't be until 2203.

Noctilucent clouds

Summer is the time of the year that we see the strange and ethereal phenomenon in the dusk and dawn skies during astronomical twilight, known as "Noctilucent clouds" (NLC's). These clouds are very high, about 50 miles above the Earth, and are usually white or silvery electric-blue in colour and are quite often seen in the summer skies above the dusk or dawn horizons of the Isle of Man. They tend to exhibit a thin wave-like pattern that indicates strong winds at this altitude.

There is some evidence that these clouds' frequency and intensity are linked to atmospheric warming. So, it is with mixed feelings that we view and marvel at these fascinating clouds. Another theory suggests they are caused by incoming meteors. Following an IOMAS meeting in June 2016, some of us managed to see some NLC's when we stayed behind to view some of the features in the summer night skies.

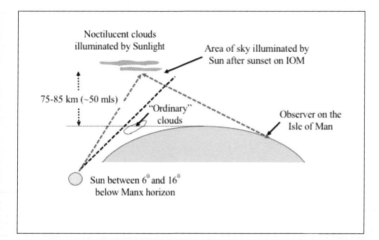

Observing
Noctilucent clouds.

In the diagram:

Noctilucent clouds
illuminated by Sunlight

Area of sky illuminated by
Sun after sunset on IOM

75-85 km (~50 mls)

"Ordinary"
clouds

Observer on the
Isle of Man

Sun between 6° and 16°
below Manx horizon

Noctilucent clouds
over the Isle of Man.
(Bill Bevan)

Noctilucent clouds
over the IOMAS
observatory. *(Dave
Storey)*

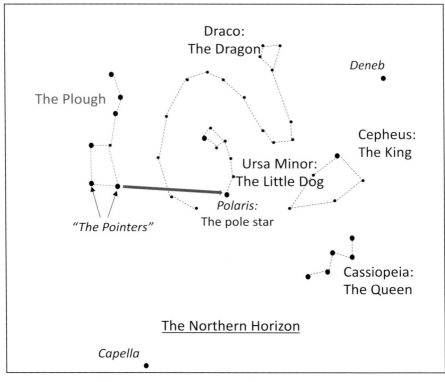

Draco:
The Dragon

Deneb

The Plough

Cepheus:
The King

Ursa Minor:
The Little Dog

Polaris:
The pole star

"The Pointers"

Cassiopeia:
The Queen

The Northern Horizon

Capella

The northern
circumpolar sky.

The northern sky in summer

The Plough is now heading down to its more familiar autumnal position. During the summer, it lies to the left of the NCP with the pointer stars of Dubhe and Merak almost level and left of Polaris. Above the north-western horizon, the distinctive shape of Cassiopeia is rising.

The Milky Way in summer

Despite the light nights, the Milky Way is at its most dramatic at this time of year, with the star clouds and dust lanes in the constellations of Sagittarius and Scorpio low on the southern horizon. The central region of the Milky Way is in this area of the sky and is seen at its best by southern hemisphere observers. Just look on a moonless night at about 10.00 PM. The Milky Way can be seen from the western horizon to the eastern horizon and passes almost directly overhead. It is at its best slightly towards the west as you look up. This is the area of the Cygnus rift. On a clear night, this can be seen as like a rip in a veil. A pair of binoculars will greatly enhance your view.

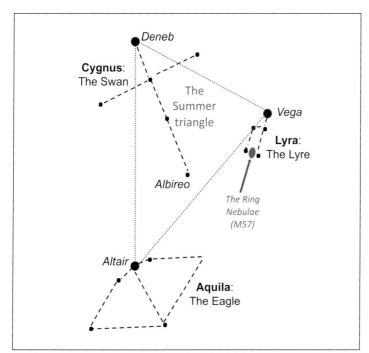

The Summer Triangle

One feature which dominates the summer sky is the asterism known as the "summer triangle". This triangle connects the bright stars Deneb in Cygnus, Vega in Lyra, and Altair in Aquila.

The relative brightness of these stars is misleading. Vega is 25 light-years away and appears to be the brightest of the three. At magnitude 0.0, it is often regarded as a "standard candle". Altair at magnitude 0.76 is even closer at 17 light-years. Deneb at magnitude 1.25 is the faintest of the three but is an estimated distance of 2,600 light-years, so it is the most luminous by far. If you placed all three at a similar distance, Deneb would far outshine Vega and Altair. Deneb's luminosity is estimated to equal 200,000 times that of our Sun.

A good eyesight test is to find the compact group of faint stars two-thirds along the line joining Vega to Altair. Here, slightly west of the distinctive constellation of Sagitta: The Arrow, lies Brocchi's Cluster. Binoculars will show the group's members form the shape of an upside-down coat hanger. This "coat hanger" cluster, like many of the other patterns described, is an asterism formed from physically unrelated stars

Opposite: The stars
of the Summer
Triangle and the
Cygnus rift in the
Milky Way. *(Ron
Strathdee)*

Cygnus: The Swan

Cygnus is a very distinctive constellation formed from the body and wings of the bird. It is often seen as the asterism of the northern cross. Mythologically Cygnus represents the swan that Jupiter turned himself into to visit Leda, the wife of the King of Sparta. Another legend states that Cygnus represents the musician Orpheus, placed in the sky adjacent to his Lyre, in the constellation Lyra. The bright star Deneb sits majestically at the head of the vertical axis of the cross. Deneb is the 19th brightest star in our night sky. However, it is the brightest of any in the list of bright stars in terms of its luminosity. At a declination of 45 degrees north, Deneb is circumpolar and can be seen throughout the year.

The star at the foot of the cross is Albireo, a glorious telescopic double star system formed from a bright yellow primary and azure-blue secondary. Finally, Cygnus contains two Messier objects M29 and M39. Both are open clusters.

Lyra: The Lyre

The Ring Nebulae
(M57) in Lyra from
the IOM. *(James
Martin)*

The second constellation in the summer triangle is to the lower right of Cygnus. The constellation of Lyra represents the harp that Apollo gave the great musician Orpheus. Vega is the 5th brightest star in our skies and is very distinctive. The nearby Ring nebula (M57) in Lyre has to be one of the

Deneb

Vega

The Cygnus rift

Altair

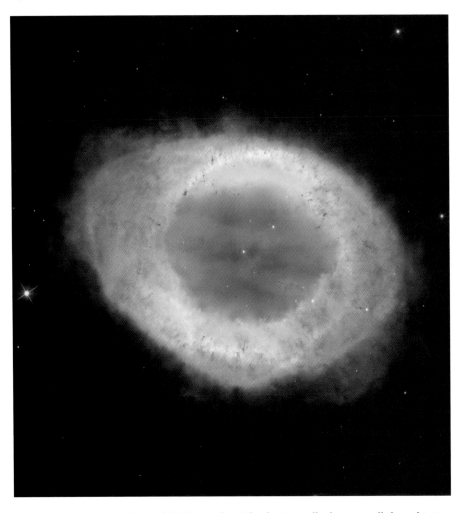

The Ring Nebulae (M57) in Lyra from the Hubble Space Telescope. *(NASA)*

most beautiful sights in the night sky. A small telescope will show this tiny ring in the heavens.

It is an expanding shell of gas that erupted from the surface of a dying star. It is 2,300 light-years away and estimated to be 1.5 light-years in diameter. As a small boy, when I saw this object, I thought it was comparable to seeing Saturn's rings through a small telescope.

The star Sheliak (Beta Lyrae) is another "Algol" type star, an eclipsing binary that varies between 3.4 to 4.3 magnitude in just under 13 days. Finally, the star Epsilon Lyrae is known as the "double-double". Viewing through a telescope reveals that the star is a double, and both of these are themselves doubles.

Aquila: The Eagle

The third constellation in the summer triangle, Aquila, is below and left of Cygnus. Straddles the celestial equator. Mythologically it represents the Eagle that held Zeus's thunderbolts. According to some versions of the legend, Zeus also turned himself into an eagle to abduct Ganymede, the cup holder of the Gods. The brightest star in Aquila, Altair at magnitude 0.76, is the 12th brightest star in the sky and is just 17 light-years away. The stars Alshain and Tarazed are roughly equidistant on each side of Altair, making it quite distinctive.

Hercules: The Strongman

To the right of the summer triangle asterism is Hercules, a faint but large constellation. Hercules, as an infant, was being fed by the Goddess Hera. However, he bit her and was pushed away, and the spilt milk formed the Milky Way. Hercules inherited great strength and power and was later tasked with undertaking 12 labours that he accomplished and was subsequently rewarded with a place in the sky for eternity.

Hercules has only two stars brighter than 3rd magnitude. Raslagethi magnitude 3.08 is a double star comprising a red star and a greenish-white star companion. Hercules is home to two globular clusters M13 and M93. M13, at magnitude 5.9, is just visible to the naked eye from a dark sky. It is over 22,000 light-years away and is regarded as one of the best open clusters in the northern sky.

Scorpio: The Scorpion

Scorpion is another constellation in the summer night sky that looks a little like the object it represents. Scorpio represents the creature that killed the mighty Orion and is placed at the opposite part of the sky to Orion, thus keeping these celestial rivals apart. Scorpio's brightest star is the distinctively red coloured Antares. The name means "rival of Mars" Antares is a massive star. Its diameter is estimated to be 946 million km (600 million miles). This is bigger than the orbit of Mars. It is over 600 light-years from the Earth. Scorpio has a distinctive tail, but its tail stars do not rise above the Manx horizon due to its southern location.

Meteor showers visible in the summer skies

August also brings us the annual spectacle of the Perseid meteor shower. The Perseids are one of the best astronomical events each year, the shower peaking on and around 12th August.

Chapter 18

Observing the Planets and Satellites

Since ancient times, it was believed that the Earth was at the centre of the universe, stationary, and the sky rotated around it. In about 3,500 BC, the ancient Egyptians believed that the Sun was carried on a boat each night and arose each morning victorious, having defeated the forces of darkness. Another interesting explanation suggested that the "flat Earth" was carried on four giant elephants, standing on the back of a giant "cosmic turtle". In recent years, this concept was resurrected by Terry Pratchett in his "Discworld" novels.

Another story relates to an Island somewhat further south and warmer than the Isle of Man. Maui was a demi-God from Polynesian mythology. Maui promised his mother he would catch the Sun and keep it in the sky, making the days longer. He climbed up a mountain, and using a rope, he lassoed the Sun. This is why Hawaii gets so much Sun. Perhaps we ought to get Manannan to do the same for the Isle of Man.

Only 500 years ago, it was still believed that the Sun moved across the sky every day, rising in the east and setting each night in the west. It was believed that the Earth itself remained stationary.

Any casual observer of the night skies may notice a small number of bright starlike objects that slowly appear to move against the background stars in the night sky. These are the planets, from the Greek word "Planetes", meaning wanderer. There are six of these, Mercury, Venus, Mars, Jupiter and Saturn and no one is credited with their discovery. Some of them moved quite quickly across the sky in a matter of days or weeks, but others moved more slowly over a period of months. Explaining the motion of these objects was a difficult task for ancient astronomers

The first model of the "Geocentric Universe" was produced by Eudoxus in 380 BC. He placed an unmoving Earth at the centre. In 343 BC Aristotle (and later Ptolomy) revised this model. The Earth was surrounded by the four fundamental elements of earth, water, air and fire. Then in increasing distances from Earth, the other objects in the solar system. The Moon, followed by the planets Mercury, Venus, the Sun, and the other planets Mars, Jupiter, and Saturn. It was clearly understood that the time they took to cross the sky indicated their increasing distance from the Earth. Aristotle's model and variations of it were accepted for nearly 2000 years.

At that time, one observation that could not be easily explained was that of "retrograde motion". The planets generally move across the sky from west to east in "direct" or "positive" motion. Retrograde motion is the name given

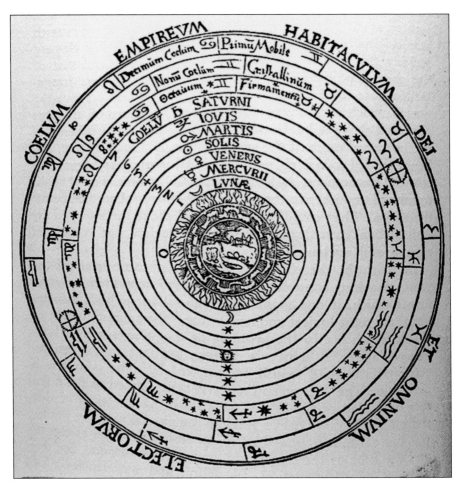

The Geocentric universe – Aristotle 343 BC.

to the phenomenon when a planet seems to slow, stop and then go backwards against a background of distant stars. This was a major stumbling block in any explanation of the cosmos.

In 140 AD, Aristotle's model was revised by Ptolemy. Ptolemy believed that the planets did not orbit the Earth from a fixed position on their orbit but instead orbited a "deferent" located on this position. The planet orbits the deferent, and the deferent orbits the Earth. The orbit of the planet around the deferent was called an "epicycle". This system explained why the planets appear to go forwards and backwards during a year. Whilst widely accepted, it did not explain why the period of retrograde motion was significantly less than the period of direct motion. It did, however, explain why a planet's brightness varied. Ptolemy's explanation was accepted for nearly 1500 years.

In 1543 *"De revolutionibus orbium coelestium"* (*On the revolutions of*

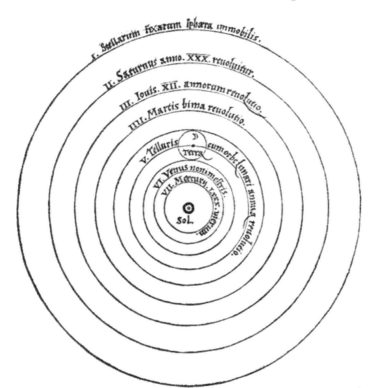

The Heliocentric
Universe –
Copernicus 1543.

heavenly spheres) was published based on the work of Polish astronomer
Nicolaus Copernicus (1473-1543). Copernicus proposed a controversial
alternative to the Geocentric Universe. The "Heliocentric Universe" in
which the Earth was not stationary but moved in an orbit around the
stationary Sun.

This proposal also suggested that the Earth not only turned on its axis
in 24 hours but also orbited the Sun annually. It is believed that his ideas
originated around 1512, but it was not published until the year of his death.
His theory had a significant influence on several other astronomers, notably
Galileo, Kepler, and Newton.

Initially, Copernicus's theory was not well received, and it took over 100
years for it to be widely accepted. Danish astronomer Tycho Brahe (1546-
1601) disagreed with the heliocentric theory and published an alternative
explanation. This was a Geocentric model system utilising elaborate
epicycles and some of Copernicus's heliocentric theory elements. Tycho
kept extensive observations and was one of the first to make, maintain and
use very accurate and detailed observations, including a conjunction of
Jupiter and Saturn in 1563, the supernova in Cassiopeia in 1572 and a
comet in 1577.

In 1580 Tycho established an observatory on the Baltic island of Hven. Here he was assisted by Johannes Kepler. Upon his death, Kepler succeeded Tycho. However, Kepler, unlike his predecessor, felt that the Copernican theory had significant merit. Using Tycho's extensive records, Kepler produced three laws of planetary motion. The first two in 1609 and the third in 1619. Whilst Copernicus's work was radical, it assumed that the planetary orbits were circular. Kepler suggested that the orbits were elliptical, not circular. It was this crucial distinction that Kepler identified and used in his work.

Kepler's laws of planetary motion

1st law: The planets move around the Sun in elliptical orbits, with the Sun at one focus of this ellipse.

2nd law: The radius of the vector joining the planet to the Sun sweeps out equal areas in equal times as the planet travels around the ellipse.

3rd law: The square of the orbital period of a planet is directionally proportional to the cube of the semi-axis major of its orbit.

In 1608 a Dutch eyeglass maker Hans Lippershey applied for a patent for a telescope. Upon learning of this invention, the Italian astronomer Galileo Galilei used such an instrument for astronomical observations and made many significant discoveries. This work led him to become a supporter of the Copernican theory. This was to cause many problems for Galileo with the ecclesiastical authorities. At one time, he was placed under house arrest. In 1633 he was forced to recant his support for the heliocentric theory under threat of torture. It is rumoured that he muttered under his breath upon recanting. *"Eppur si muove" (yet it (the Earth) moves)*.

In 1681, Isaac Newton, who had obtained his post at Cambridge due to the recognition of his talents by the nephew of Manx Bishop Isaac Barrow, published his book "Principia". Today, Principia is still regarded as one of the most significant scientific publications ever published. Newton's "discovery" of gravity led to the final confirmation and validity of the heliocentric universe.

The significance of this discovery of the true nature of the orbital mechanics of the solar system was quite profound. Before this date, the subjects of astronomy and astrology ran side by side. This was because vague models of the cosmos made the ability to predict the exact observational positions of the planets extremely difficult. This linked in well with the astrologers who predicted all manner of things. The discovery that the Earth and the other bodies move in elliptical orbits around the Sun meant that the position of any planetary body could be determined with precision. Consequently, all observational characteristics, including retrograde motion,

The author with Dr Mukesh Sharma (astronomer and astrologer) at Jantar Mantar.

elongations, conjunctions, and opposition, could be satisfactorily explained. Today Kepler's laws of planetary motion are used extensively to calculate orbits of celestial bodies and spacecraft in the cosmos.

For the important roles these three individuals played in our understanding of the heavens, Copernicus, Tycho and Kepler all have craters named after them on the Moon. Galileo was not ignored; he has a whole family of Moons (Io, Europa, Ganymede and Callisto) named after him orbiting Jupiter.

Consequently, the subjects of astrology and astronomy parted company and became two different disciplines with a common link.

In 2017, through my Fellowship of the Royal Astronomical Society, I was able to undertake a private visit to the famous observatory of Jantar Mantar in Jaipur, India. I was given a fascinating tour of the various astronomical instruments in the observatory, which was completed in 1738. My host was Dr Mukesh Sharma. During the tour, I was astounded to learn he had two separate professional qualifications in astronomy and astrology!

Retrograde motion

The Earth takes a year, or 365.25 days, to orbit the Sun. The outer planets have years that are longer than ours as they are further away. This means that the Earth seems to catch up with them. So once a year, they appear to move backwards or retrograde, as seen against a background of distant stars. The same phenomenon can also be seen with Mercury and Venus. As their orbits are nearer the Sun, they catch up and pass the Earth.

Conjunction

A conjunction is defined as when a planet is close or "conjoined" with another object in the solar system. As seen from the Earth, all the planets in the solar system, except for Mars, go through conjunction with the Sun at least once a year. The two inferior planets (Mercury and Venus) have two different types of conjunctions. When they pass between the Earth and Sun, they go through "inferior conjunction". When they are behind the Sun, they go through "superior conjunction". Mars, Jupiter, Saturn, Uranus and Neptune (collectively known as superior planets) all have superior conjunctions, but this is usually just termed as "conjunctions". As the planet Mars orbits the Sun in two years, it comes to conjunction every other year. When an inner planet goes through inferior conjunction, it may, if the orbit of the planet and Earth coincide, "transit" the Sun.

The name conjunction also applies to when two or more planets appear close to each other in the sky. This is just a line of sight effect when a nearer object is seen in the same part of the sky as a more distant object. This is similar to the effect of seeing the Moon rising next to a tree or building. The two are a considerable distance apart, but they appear close in that part of the sky.

Opposition

Opposition is the name given to the opposite of conjunction and only applies to the superior planets. Opposition occurs when a planet at midnight is in a location exactly opposite the Sun's position. All the outer planets, Jupiter, Saturn, Uranus and Neptune, have an annual opposition, but Mars again is the exception. The Martian year is 687 days; it takes almost twice as long to orbit the Sun. This means that it also comes to conjunction and to opposition every 25 months. Another observational feature for the planets as seen from the Earth is "quadrature", when a superior planet is 90 degrees from the Sun.

Elongation

Elongations only apply to the inferior planets, Mercury and Venus. Being inside Earth's orbit, they can never appear very far from the Sun. They are seen alternately in the evening and morning sky. The elongation in the evening sky is called "greatest eastern elongation" (GEE). In the morning sky, the opposite occurs, and "greatest western elongation" (GWE) occurs.

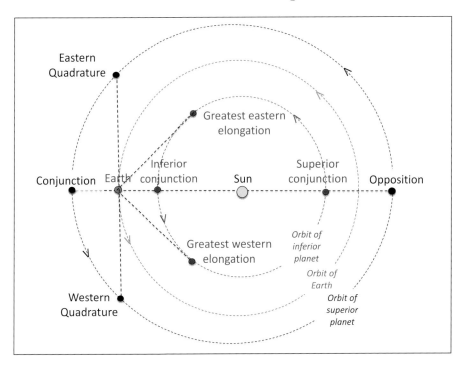

This can be confusing because we see eastern elongation in the west after sunset and western elongation in the morning sky in the east before sunrise. At eastern elongation in the evening sky, the planet is east of the Sun, but at the western elongation in the morning sky, it will be west of the Sun. I always recall which is which by using the middle letter. In GEE, the "E" refers to evening, whilst in GWE, the middle "W" is an upside-down "M" for morning.

If we were observing from Mars, the Earth would be an inferior planet and elongate from the Sun at GEE and GWE. Subsequently Earth can also transit the Sun. Such a transit occurred in 1984. The next one is in 2084.

If you are confused with the terminology, any planet inside Earth's orbit is termed an "inferior planet". A planet outside Earth's orbit is termed a "superior planet". The planets Mercury, Venus, Earth and Mars, are all "inner planets". Jupiter, Saturn, Uranus and Neptune are all "outer planets".

- **Mercury** and **Venus** are inferior, inner planets
- **Earth** is an inner planet
- **Mars** is an inner, superior planet
- **Jupiter, Saturn, Uranus** and **Neptune** are outer, superior planets

Observational characteristics of the planets.

Observing Mercury (*Mercur*)

"Morning and evening stars" have been seen throughout history. These are the names given to the appearance of Mercury or Venus in the sky before sunrise or after sunset. Mercury, being much smaller, is much fainter, and consequently, is difficult to see. In ancient times it was believed that there were two planets in Mercury's location. Mercury was seen in the evening sky, but another planet, Apollo, was seen in the morning sky. It is uncertain when it was realised that they were the same planet. Eventually, the planet Apollo was consigned to history and sometimes regarded as one of the "ghosts of the solar system".

The first recorded observation of Mercury was in 265 BC, when Mercury was recorded as being just one lunar diameter away from a line joining stars Beta and Delta Scorpii. Mercury, like its fellow interior and inner companion planet, Venus can only be seen in the sky just after sunset or just before sunrise. Its location as the closest planet to the Sun means that it can never elongate further than 28 degrees from the Sun. Despite shining brighter than any star in the night sky at a maximum magnitude of -1.8. Mercury will never be seen in a dark sky other than during a total Solar eclipse.

Mercury is the smallest solar system planet at only 4,878 km (3031 miles) in diameter. Its year is 88 days, and it rotates on its axis in 58.6 days. Mercury's orbit is synchronised in what is termed "spin-orbit resonance". It rotates on its axis three times for every two revolutions of the Sun. The orbit is the most highly eccentric of the planets, which causes the planet's elongations to vary from 18 to 28 degrees.

Being the closest planet to the Sun, Mercury is also the fastest moving. Its orbital speed is 47.4 km/s (or 107,150 mph). How appropriate that a depiction of Mercury as the Greek Hermes, the fleet-footed messenger of the Gods, adorns the IOM TT motorcycling trophies. The Earth is no slowcoach at an orbital speed of 30 km/s (or 66,660 mph). It would take just over two seconds to travel the distance of the TT course at this speed, assuming it was a straight line.

The orbit of Mercury is inclined at seven degrees from the ecliptic, which affects the visibility of this innermost planet.

Given the eccentricity of Mercury's orbit, Mercury can be seen alternatively in the morning and evening sky at approximately six-week intervals. When Mercury is at inferior conjunction, it can "transit" the Sun (see chapter 9).

All the above characteristics mean that seeing Mercury in the night sky is never easy. Many astronomers have never seen it. Try a few days before or after elongation to spot it for yourself. Look in the evening sky after sunset and see if you can see a "star" in the twilight sky. Binoculars will help but, be very careful *never* to look directly anywhere near the Sun

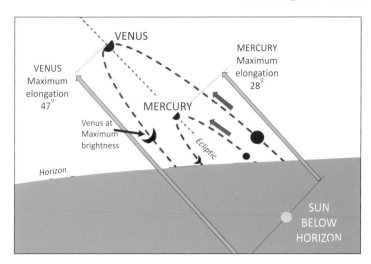

The evening elongations of Mercury and Venus.

under any circumstances. You could severely damage your eyesight. I always advise never to look for Mercury (or any other object) when the Sun is above the horizon. You can also try the same method during morning elongations before sunrise. The best way to find Mercury is when the Moon or another planet is in the same part of the sky. Using Venus is a great way to see Mercury.

The Moon, Mercury and Venus above Peel Castle – March 2018. *(Ron Strathdee)*

When Venus is visible in the sky and is joined by Mercury, it can be an excellent guide. Of course, the same applies to Mars, Jupiter and Saturn, but the view of the bright Venus and Mercury together in the sky is a beautiful sight.

Observing Venus *(Bayntag)*

In a similar way to its smaller neighbour Mercury, Venus was initially thought to be two different planets in the morning and evening sky. But like Mercury which had two names Mercury and Apollo, Venus also had two distinct names. It was seen as Hesperus in the evening sky and Phosphorus in the morning sky.

Venus is 12,104 km (7,521 miles) in diameter, very similar to the Earth at 12,756 km (7,926 miles). Venus is the second planet out from the Sun. At 41 million km (25 million miles) and is our second nearest celestial neighbour. After the Moon, Venus can be the brightest object in our night sky. It orbits the Sun in 224 days, and of all of the planets, it has the least eccentric orbit. Venus elongates between 45 and 47 degrees from the Sun. It takes Venus nearly 18 months (584 days) to move from evening elongation, through to inferior conjunction, to morning conjunction, to superior conjunction and then back to evening elongation.

Crescent Venus –
21st May 2004.
(Dave Storey)

Seeing Venus in our night skies is probably one of the easiest of all astronomical sights. Before and after elongation, Venus can be seen in a dark sky shining like a beacon before sunrise or after sunset for quite a few months. Venus is bright enough on occasion to be seen in daylight when at elongation. But remember never look anywhere near the Sun.

When Galileo first looked at Venus through a telescope, he realised that Venus, like the Moon, shows distinct phases. This reinforced his view about the validity of the heliocentric nature of the solar system. Venus is totally cloud-covered, so its reflectivity or "albedo" is very high. Venus is at its brightest a few weeks after evening elongation or before morning elongation when it is closest and can be seen as a large crescent. Venus can be as bright as magnitude -4.4 and is bright enough to cast a shadow.

As with Mercury, at inferior conjunction, Venus can transit the Sun. These occur in pairs, the last pair being in 2004 and 2012, and the next pair will be in 2117 and 2125 (See Chapter nine).

When Venus appears in our skies around Christmas time, many people ask whether this may have been the "Christmas star". Whilst unlikely, Venus may well have had a role as one of the objects seen around 2000 years ago foretelling the birth of Christ (See chapter ten).

Observing the Moon *(Eayst)*

The Moon has been an object of fascination since humans first looked up at the sky. There is much evidence that the Moon has an impact on the human psyche. Many people believe that human behaviour is linked to the lunar cycle. Subjects such as lunacy, fertility, werewolves and others have been studied extensively throughout the ages. In the UK in the nineteenth century, defence lawyers on occasion tried to use the "lunar defence" or "guilty by reason of the Full Moon" to justify that clients were not accountable for their actions under the Moon's influence.

One of my work colleagues at MNH was a keen gardener, and he was adamant that planting seeds must coincide with the waxing Moon. There is anecdotal evidence that some surgeons prefer not to operate around the time of a Full Moon. There is also evidence of a correlation between increased occurrences of epilepsy and accident rates being more prevalent around the time of the Full Moon. However, it is now believed that this correlation is more to do with the overall brightness of the night sky in the period before, during and after a Full Moon.

The Moon has inspired many artists and writers throughout history. In Viking mythology, the Moon reflecting on the sea was regarded as the road to Valhalla. One of the first-ever works of fiction about the Moon was written in about 150 AD by the Greek Lucian of Samosata. In his work, "True History," he talks about a group of travellers taken by a whirlwind up to the

Full (Super) Moon
rising over Langness
– 26th May 2021.
(Ron Strathdee)

Moon. They became involved in a war between the King of the Moon and the King of the Sun over the colonisation of the morning star. Eventually, peace reigns and Lucian goes on to describe life on the Moon.

In 1865 Jules Verne wrote "A Journey from the Earth to the Moon". A novel referred to in July 1969 by Apollo 11 commander Neil Armstrong on their way back from the first lunar landing mission.

"A hundred years ago, Jules Verne wrote a book about a voyage to the Moon. The spaceship Columbia took off from Florida and landed in the Pacific Ocean after completing a trip to the Moon. It seems appropriate to us to share with you some of the reflections of the crew, as the modern-day Columbia completes its rendezvous with the planet Earth and the same Pacific Ocean tomorrow".

In 1901 H.G.Wells's book "From the Earth to the Moon" was about a British lunar mission. They used a great invention to reach the Moon, called "Cavorite". This was anti-gravity paint. You just paint it on, and then when it dries, off you go! I understand SpaceX would like to make something similar. There was a film of the same name released in 1964. And the scriptwriter was none other than Manx author Nigel Kneale. Kneale became very well known for his "Quatermass" novels. At the end of the film, the US land on the Moon only to find a faded Union Jack on the surface.

Unlike all other planets in the solar system, the Earth is unique, having just one large natural satellite, the Moon. The Moon orbits the Earth and its rotational period is equal to its revolution period of 27.3 days. As a result, the same face is always turned to the Earth. We can, however, see just under 60% of the lunar surface due to a phenomenon known as "libration".

The Moon is 3,475 km in diameter (2,159 miles). This compares to the Earth at 12,756 km (7,926 miles). This makes the Earth-Moon system the largest planet-moon system by ratio in the solar system. Strictly speaking, the system is a dual planetary system. This is because the Earth and Moon orbit a common point or "barycentre". In the Earth-Moon system, the barycentre is about 1,000 km (621 miles) below the Earth's surface.

As the Moon orbits the Earth, we get to see lunar phases, and this gives us a cycle of thirteen Full Moons in a year. As there are four seasons on Earth each year, when a season contains four Full Moons, the fourth one is called a "Blue Moon". There is also a "Black Moon the name given to the equivalent second New Moon in a season. A more popular definition of a Blue (or Black) Moon is when two Full (or New) Moons occur in one month, but the previous definition is older and more accurate.

As seen from the Earth, the Moon has a mean apparent diameter of 31.5 arc minutes (just over half a degree). At "perigee" (closest to Earth), it can be 34.1 arc minutes, whilst at "apogee" (furthest from Earth), it can be as little as 29.3 arc minutes. This is similar to the Sun's apparent diameter, which is why we see eclipses (See chapter nine).

There is an interesting experiment you can do. Next time you see a Full Moon near the horizon, imagine how many would fit around the whole horizon. When I ask this question, most people think, a few hundred or maybe 300 or so. The answer is 720 because the Moon is just half a degree wide. 360 multiplied by 0.5 = 720. This is all part of what is known as the "Moon illusion". When we see a Full Moon close to the horizon, it may be adjacent to a tree, building, or other distant objects and it will appear much larger than it really is. You can prove this for yourself. Next time you see the Moon, you will find it is always no bigger than your little fingernail at arm's length, no matter where you see it in the sky.

The Moon orbits the Earth at a mean distance of 384,400 km (238,855 miles), but because the lunar orbit is an ellipse, at perigee, the Earth to Moon is 356,410 km (221,462 miles) whilst at apogee, it is 400,697 km (248,981 miles). There is a relatively new but unofficial expression that has come into popular culture, the "Supermoon". A Supermoon is defined as when the Full or New Moon occurs within 90 degrees of perigee or apogee.

A Supermoon can appear up to 14% bigger at perigee than at apogee. This difference also means that the brightness of a supermoon can be up to 30% brighter than a "Micro-moon" or "Wimpy-moon". Statistically, there can be three or four supermoons a year. The biggest Supermoon since 1948 occurred on 14th November 2016. There will be a closer one on 25th November 2034, and there will be an even still closer one on 6th December 2052.

The proper name for a Supermoon is "perigee-syzygy". The name Supermoon was first used by astrologer Richard Nolle in 1979. Many astronomers do not like the name. However, others feel that if it makes people look up and appreciate any celestial object, it has to be beneficial to the subject of astronomy.

Supermoon compared to Micro or Wimpy Moon.

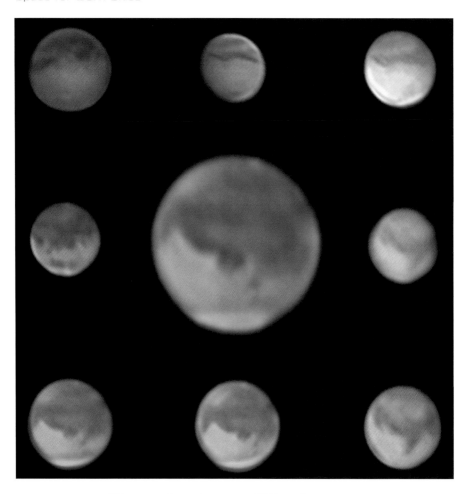

The differing appearance of Mars during the 2005 opposition. *(Dave Storey)*

Observing Mars *(Mart)*

Mars is the fourth planet from the Sun and is 6,779 km (4,221 miles) in diameter, roughly half the size of Earth. The Martian day a "sol" is 24 hours and 37 minutes. Mars has a similar axial tilt as the Earth, at just over 25 degrees, so there are seasons on Mars, but the Martian seasons last twice as long. Thus, resident Martians enjoy a six-month summer, but on the other hand, they also get a six-month winter!

Mars can, at opposition, be seen as bright as magnitude –2.8. It will be seen for many months before and after opposition but fades quickly as the distance from Earth to Mars changes. It shines with a distinctive red colour. The Martian orbit has a high eccentricity, and so the distance and brightness from Earth at oppositions can vary considerably. Mars can also be seen to have a gibbous phase when at quadrature.

The minimum distance from Earth to Mars is 0.37 AU or 55.7 million km (34.6 million miles). This occurs at a close opposition. When Mars is at its furthest from the Earth, the distance is 2.68 AU or 401 million km (250 million miles). The apparent diameter of Mars from Earth varies from 25.1 arc seconds in opposition to only 3.5 arc seconds at its maximum distance from Earth. In 2003, Mars was closer to the Earth than it had been for over 60,000 years. This led to allegations that Mars would be as big as a Full Moon. This is certainly not the case. It is speculated that it came about because someone thought that 25 arc seconds was similar to the lunar diameter of 31 arc minutes.

We have had a fascination with Mars for many years, but it was not until the first telescopic views of the red planet were undertaken that it was seriously suggested that Mars may support life. In 1877 the Italian astronomer Schiaparelli drew a map of the Martian surface. He indicated that he could see streaks on the Martian surface, which he termed "canalli". This translated into the English word "canal". As a consequence, this led to the idea that Mars may have intelligent life. Similar observations of features on the Marian disc led to astronomer Percival Lowell, in 1894, despite not having seen these canals for himself, stating:

"Speculation has been singularly fruitful as to what these markings on one of our nearest celestial neighbours in space may mean. We are looking upon

Headline from the New York Times – Monday 31st October 1938.

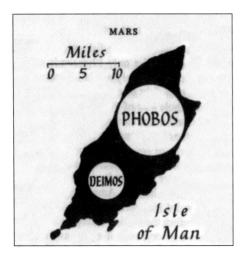

MARS

Miles
0 5 10

PHOBOS

DEIMOS

Isle
of Man

From Patrick
Moore's book.

the result of the work of some sort of intelligent beings…. The amazing network on Mars hints that one planet besides our own is actually inhabited now".

In 1900 the Guzman prize was announced in Paris. An award of 100,000 French Francs would be awarded to the first communication with extra-terrestrial beings. Mars, however, was explicitly excluded.

In 1938, Orson Welles read extracts from H.G.Wells's book "War of the Worlds" during a radio broadcast, which led to widespread panic. Many listeners believed they were listening to an actual Martian invasion.

In 1965, NASA's Mariner 4 spacecraft successfully flew by Mars but found no sign of life. It is now believed that whilst primitive life may have evolved on Mars, the hostile environment of Mars is no longer able to support it. So today, scientists are concentrating on looking for signs of primitive life that may have evolved before becoming extinct by the changing Martian environment.

With modern telescopes and subsequent spacecraft observations, it has been realised that the streaks on the surface, thought initially to be vegetation growing alongside the canals, are just surface features and dust storms. The size at opposition enables the Martian polar ice caps and various features to be easily seen on the Martian surface using a telescope. Mars has two Moons, Deimos and Phobos. These are both very small and only 12.6 and 22.2 km (7.8 and 13.8 miles) in diameter, respectively. Both are believed to be captured asteroids. In one of Patrick Moore's earlier books, he used the Isle of Man to show the size of the two Martian Moons.

Observing Jupiter

Jupiter is the largest planet in our solar system. It is 143,884 km (89,400 miles) in diameter and orbits the Sun at a mean distance of 5.2 AU. or 778.3 million km (483.6 million miles). It can shine as bright as magnitude -2.9, second only to Venus. As Jupiter is an outer planet, it can be seen all night before and after opposition. The Jovian year is 12.6 Earth years. Consequently, every year Earth catches up with the slower moving Jupiter every 13 months, like a fast car on the inside track of a racetrack.

An interesting fact about Jovian oppositions is that its orbit means that it passes through one of the 12 signs of the zodiac each year. This is believed to have been one of the major factors in the credibility of astrology. To have

Galileo's observations from 1610.

this bright giant of the solar system appear to have an ordered regular passage through one of these significant constellations once a year was thought to be astrologically significant.

A significant factor in Galileo's support of the Copernican heliocentric explanation was his telescopic views of Jupiter. His observations revealed that Jupiter had up to four small "stars" that always appear very close to the planet.

On 7th January 1610, Galileo saw three of these "stars" over several nights using his new telescope. He noticed that they moved in a different direction than the background stars but appeared to move with some consistency in relation to each other and Jupiter. A few days later, he saw a fourth "star" showing the same orbital characteristics. On 15th January 1610, he concluded that they were not stars but natural satellites of the planet Jupiter. He published his discovery in March 1610.

Galileo initially labelled them I to IV using Roman numerals. I being the

The Moon and Jupiter and the four Galilean Moons – 15th July 2015. *(Dave Storey)*

closest and IV the furthest from Jupiter. They have since then always been referred to as the Galilean satellites in Galileo's honour. Similarly, the first spacecraft to orbit Jupiter was also named Galileo. The Danish astronomer Johannes Kepler suggested the names Io, Europa, Ganymede, and Callisto from mythological figures associated with Jupiter. However, the names were not in widespread usage until the early nineteenth century.

Jupiter – 6th April 2004. *(Dave Storey)*

You can easily see up to four of these moons through a small telescope or pair of binoculars. They are all bright enough to be seen by the naked eye, but the glare of Jupiter makes this very difficult. The outermost two, Ganymede and Callisto, may be seen when they are at their furthest from Jupiter. It is a fascinating sight looking at the Galilean Moons. Sometimes you will only see two or three of them as the others may be in front of or behind Jupiter. As you look at them, spare a thought for Galileo using a primitive telescope with which he made this important discovery over 400 years ago. Using various spacecraft, we now believe that Jupiter has 80 moons.

It is also possible with a small telescope to see on Jupiter at least two distinctive darker cloud belts, the North and South Equatorial Belts. Using a larger telescope, you may also be able to see Jupiter's Great Red Spot. This was first observed in 1831, so we know it has existed for at least 150 years.

In recent years the spot seems to be shrinking, so it's under a lot of scrutiny at present.

In 1992 Jupiter was a major subject in the media. It was realised that Comet Levy-Shoemaker 9 had been disturbed by the gravity of Jupiter and was going to strike Jupiter in 1994. The resultant impact of the comet was observed by the orbiting Hubble Space telescope and the approaching Galileo spacecraft.

Observing Saturn *(Sarn)*

Saturn is the second-largest planet in the solar system. Despite its distance, at opposition, at magnitude -0.8, it exceeds all but the two brightest stars Sirius (-1.4) and Canopus (-0.75), in the night sky.

Saturn is 120,536 km (74,897 miles) in diameter and orbits the Sun at a mean distance of 9.5 AU. or 1427 million km (886.7 million miles). As Saturn is an outer planet, it can also be seen all night before and after opposition. Saturn orbits the Sun in 29.4 years. Consequently, it passes through one of the 12 signs of the zodiac approximately every two years.

When viewed through a small telescope, Saturn displays a magnificent ring system. While not as bright at opposition as its fellow solar system residents Venus, Jupiter or Mars, Saturn is probably the most amazing sight most people will ever see in the night sky. In astronomy, it is often said: "*Show a child Saturn through a telescope, and they will be hooked on astronomy for life*". This was certainly the case for me: the sight of this jewel in the sky with its ring system is quite astounding. At the IOMAS observatory in Foxdale, we still get a real buzz from showing visitors Saturn: the wows and oohs! are priceless. It used to be said that Saturn was the most beautiful planet in the solar system, and whilst this has now been surpassed by seeing stunning images of

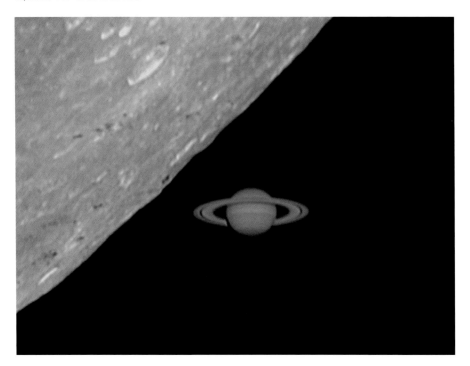

Saturn and the Moon from the IOM – 2nd March 2007. *(Dave Storey)*

the Earth from space, I, for one, still regard Saturn as one of the most beautiful objects in the night sky.

It was Galileo in 1610 who first saw Saturn through a telescope, but he could not understand what it was he was seeing. He wrote:

"The planet Saturn is not one alone but is composed of three which almost touch one another and never move with respect to one another. They are arranged in a line parallel to the zodiac, and the middle one is three times the size of the lateral ones".

He was surprised to observe two years later that these attendant globes had disappeared, and he wrote:

"Are the lesser stars consumed after the manner of solar spots, has Saturn devoured his children? The unexpected nature of the event, the weakness of my understanding and the fear of being mistaken has greatly confounded me".

We now know that Saturn's systems of rings are inclined to the ecliptic. Twice every Saturnian year, as seen from Earth, we pass through this "ring plane". Unfortunately for Galileo, one of these ring plane crossings occurred in 1612/13.

Galileo never solved the mystery, and many other astronomers had great difficulty with the enigma that Saturn presented. It was not until 1655 that Danish astronomer Christian Huygens using a much-improved telescope

Early drawings of
Saturn by Galileo.

Galileo first sketch
1610

Better telescope
1616

Published engraving
1623

concluded that these companions or arms extending from Saturn were a
ring system.

Around this time, if a scientist wanted to prove they had deduced a
particular theory but needed to test it further before formal publication,
they would publish an anagram. Huygens published the following anagram.

"aaaaaaacccccdeeeeeghiiiiiiilllllmmnnnnnnnnnnnooooppqrrrsttttttuuuu"

When rearranged, this becomes in Latin: *"Annulo cingitur tenui plano
nusquam cohaerente ad eclipticam inclinator"*. Which translated means:

Ring aspect change
between 2005 and
2007. *(Dave Storey)*

Above left: The author's iPhone image of Saturn.

Above right: The author with Dave Storey and Graham Gordon.

"It is surrounded by a ring thin plane, nowhere attached, inclined to the ecliptic".

A few years later, in 1658, Sir Christopher Wren, a keen astronomer, proposed that the phenomenon of Saturn's Rings was due to: *"An elliptical corona, meeting the globe in two places rotating with Saturn once every sidereal period".* However, Once Wren heard of Huygens explanation, he abandoned his theory. Incidentally, between 1675 and 1710, Wren built St Pauls Cathedral and used black Pooil Vaaish marble from the Isle of Man for part of the flooring.

For many years it was believed that Jupiter had the most moons in the solar system. However, in recent years it has been discovered that Saturn has at least 82 compared to Jupiter's 79. Saturn's largest moon Titan is the largest moon in the solar system and is easily seen using a small telescope. Titan is of particular interest as it has an atmosphere. In 1997 NASA launched their "Cassini" spacecraft which successfully orbited Saturn from 2004 to 2017. On arrival at Saturn, it released the ESA lander, "Huygens," which landed successfully on Titan and sent back amazing photographs from the surface of methane lakes and mountains.

On 19th July 2013, the Cassini spacecraft took a picture of the Earth from Saturn, and astronomers were asked to image Saturn at the same time. So, I took a photograph by just holding my camera phone up to the eyepiece of the IOMAS societies telescope at the observatory. It shows just how distinctive and easy the rings are to see.

Observing Uranus

Opposite: Cassini image of the Earth from near Saturn – 19th July 2013. *(NASA)*

Until the middle of the eighteenth century, there were only six known planets in the solar system. As telescopic astronomy developed, Uranus was discovered by William Herschel on 13th March 1781 from his small back garden observatory in Bath, England. Uranus is 51,118 km (31,763 miles) in diameter and is the 3rd largest planet in our solar system. At a mean

distance from the Sun of 19.2 AU. or 2,869 million km (1.78 million miles), the discovery of Uranus effectively doubled the size of the known solar system. Uranus takes 84 years to orbit the Sun and so comes to opposition just over once a year. Uranus is so far away that it is never brighter than 5.6 magnitude. At opposition, it is just visible to the naked eye. Records show that Uranus was seen in 1690 but was mistaken for a star and given the designation 34 Tauri. Upon discovery, it was realised that its orbit was not quite as expected. This indicated that another large astronomical body was causing a wobble or perturbation to its orbit. This led to a search for another planet beyond the orbit of Uranus.

Observing Neptune

The story of the discovery of the planet Neptune is a fascinating tale of ineptitude, international cooperation, along with political intrigue.

In 1845 a Cambridge University astronomer, John Couch Adams, using the perturbations in Uranus's orbit, calculated the position of an 8th planet in the solar system. In October 1845. Adams reported his predictions to James Challis, the director of the Cambridge Observatory. He also gave his predictions to the Astronomer Royal Sir George Airey. However, both failed to follow up on Adams's predictions. In November 1845, the French astronomer U.J.J. LeVerrier calculated the position of this object. Upon learning of LeVerrier's work, Airey, in July 1846 instructed James Challis, to search for the planet. It is recorded that the unsuccessful search was carried out with a *"strange lack of energy"*. On 23rd September 1846, at the Berlin Observatory, the German astronomer Johann Galle and his assistant Henri D'Arrest, using a new star catalogue, found this missing object.

As a consequence, the solar system almost doubled in size again. Adams, back in the UK, was understandably aggrieved that his "discovery" had been ignored. An international incident ensued, with the UK and French authorities each claiming that it was their discovery. Eventually, it was agreed that the planet was co-discovered by all four men.

Neptune is 50,538 km (31,402 miles) in diameter and orbits the Sun at a mean distance of 30.0 AU. or 4,496 million km (2,793 million miles). Neptune takes 164 years to orbit the Sun and comes to opposition just a few days over 12 months. Neptune's maximum magnitude is 7.7 and so can only be seen using optical aid.

Dwarf Planets

The perturbations that caused the wobble in Uranus's orbit were still not fully explained by the presence of Neptune, and Neptune also had a similar wobble. This indicated that there must be yet another body further out. In 1930 following an extensive search, US astronomer Clyde Tombaugh using the Lowell observatory in Arizona, discovered Pluto, what was then called the 9th planet in the solar system. Pluto is, however, very small and with a diameter of just 2,376 km (1,476 miles), and was, up until 2006 was regarded as the smallest planet in the solar system. Pluto also has an eccentric orbit and, at perihelion, is actually closer to the Sun than Neptune. Pluto's mean distance from the Sun is 39.5 AU. or 5.9 billion km (3.6 billion miles). Its maximum magnitude is 14 and is only visible using large telescopes. Following the discovery of several other what is known trans Neptunian objects (TNO's). In August 2006, the International Astronomical Union (IAU) decreed that a planet must fulfil specific criteria. By definition. A planet has to:

1. Orbit the Sun
2. Have sufficient mass to assume a spherical shape
3. Have cleared its orbit of any other material

Whilst Pluto has met the first two criteria, it has not cleared its orbit. As a result, the IAU created a new category of objects known as "Dwarf planets". Including Pluto, there are five dwarf planets Haumea, Makemake, and Eris, and the largest object in the asteroid belt Ceres. However, several other TNO's Gonggong, Quaoar, Sedna and Orcus, are generally also regarded as Dwarf Planets.

The decision to "downgrade" Pluto was not popularly received. For some time, there was a campaign to restore Pluto to full planetary status. This was led by, amongst others, NASA. The New Horizons spacecraft was launched to Pluto in January 2006 to fly by the planet in July 2015. NASA went on record as stating: "*Pluto was a planet when we launched, and it still is!*" The flyby of Pluto was a great success, but Pluto's planetary status remains unchanged.

In 2016. following extensive work, a team of astronomers at the California Institute of Technology (Caltech) published details of an as yet undiscovered further object in the outer solar system, which they again had calculated. The small size of Pluto and other Kuiper Belt objects still did not explain the orbital perturbations of Uranus and Neptune's orbits. This undiscovered object is thought to be similar in size to Neptune in a highly eccentric orbit.

Observing satellites

Since the dawn of the space age on 4th October 1957, artificial satellites have been orbiting the Earth. On occasion, some of the brighter ones can be seen in the night sky. We have photographic evidence of only the second-ever satellite, Sputnik 2, in the Manx night skies. It was seen over Ramsey in November 1957 (see chapter two, page 22).

In April 2020, it was estimated that there were over 30,000 objects in orbit around the Earth. Any such object larger than 25 metres (82 feet) in size will be visible to the naked eye as the sunlight reflects off its surface. These will be seen as small "stars" moving across the night sky. I recall seeing in 1960 from my home in Liverpool in 1960 a huge reflective balloon, "Echo 1", at 30 metres in diameter (100 feet), the satellite was deployed as a passive communication satellite. This was a precursor to the well-known "Telstar," immortalised by the popular record by the Tornados in 1962. Since then, observing satellites in the night sky has become part of everyday life. If you go outside a few hours after sunset or before sunrise, it will probably only take 15 minutes or so before you will see one passing through the night sky.

The largest and brightest of these visible objects is the International Space Station (ISS), which regularly passes across our skies. The ISS was assembled in orbit between 1998 and 2011 and has been continually occupied since November 2000. It orbits the Earth at an altitude of 400 km (250 miles). It moves at a speed of 27,724 kmph (17,226 mph) and can be seen as a very bright "star" crossing our skies in about four to five minutes. The ISS is 100 metres (328 feet) across and 88 metres (290 feet) long, nearly four times larger than the former Russian space station Mir. During TT week in 1994, I was on Douglas Promenade watching the firework display. I spotted an object moving from west to east above the exploding fireworks. When I went home, I looked up what it was and discovered it was Mir, the Soviet Space station with three cosmonauts on board. Perhaps they were looking down at us that night?

ISS pass over the IOMAS -1st June 2016. *(Graham Gordon)*

On the 1st June 2016, the IOMAS hosted a visit by Nicole and Chris Stott.

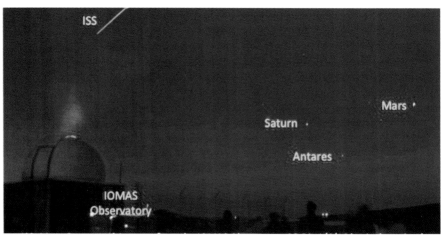

It was a clear night following the meeting, and we were aware that the ISS would be visible. So, we all went outside and saw the ISS and the planets Saturn and Mars and the giant red star Antares.

During any stargazing session, I enjoy pointing out the ISS. A few years ago, I had my first class at the UCM. I knew that the ISS would be visible at about 7.10 PM. that night. So, I introduced myself to the class and then took them all outside, and we all saw the ISS passing across our sky very clearly from the car park. I told them that I had arranged it through NASA just for them!

Another feature about seeing the ISS is that you can see more than one pass in a night. It orbits the Earth in just over 90 minutes, so it is possible to see it pass over and then again 90 minutes later. I recall one Boxing day at a party taking everyone outside to see it. We all then came back out 90 minutes later and saw it again. Quite often, especially on the second of two passes, the ISS will suddenly fade and disappear as it goes into the Earth's shadow. It is possible to get up to five passes in one night during mid-summer. This is when it passes over two or three times in the evening sky, and then two or three passes in the morning sky. I have managed to see four in a night, but not a fifth.

Before the Space Shuttle's retirement in 2011, it was possible to observe the much smaller (and fainter) Shuttle after launch before it rendezvoused and docked with the ISS. The same applies to other spacecraft approaching the ISS, but as they are significantly smaller than the Space Shuttle, they are not as bright and thus more difficult to observe.

Because of its size, the ISS at magnitude -4.1 can be almost as bright as the planet Venus at magnitude -4.4. By comparison, the Space Shuttle was as bright as magnitude -2.5. In contrast, the Dragon, Starliner and Orion spacecraft will be about magnitude +3.0 at their brightest. One spacecraft that is not visible from the Isle of Man is the Hubble Space Telescope. This is at a much lower orbital inclination and is only visible from 25 degrees north or south of the equator. A few years ago, in Sri Lanka, I managed to see it whilst on holiday. It was quite faint, only about magnitude 3.5. Still, I was delighted to have done so and stood there in awe, watching the spacecraft that has given us so many spectacular photos of the cosmos.

One newer satellite class visible in our skies is the SpaceX "Starlink" satellites. These are launched 60 at a time. It is intended to have over 3,000 in orbit, to establish a global communication network. They can currently be seen as a chain of satellites crossing the night sky. There is some concern about these being a problem for astronomers. The quantity may mean that some astronomical photographs may be "photobombed" by them crossing the field of view. SpaceX is taking steps to minimise the problem, including darkening the reflective surfaces.

Many websites and apps give details about what and when satellites will be visible. They all let you input your home location and are very easy and quick to use. If you are outside stargazing and see a satellite in the night sky, note the time and direction, and you can then look it up and identify what you saw. Every so often there will be a space mission that captures the public imagination. If the orbital inclination and timing are favourable, it may well be seen from our latitude in the night sky.

Chapter 19

Astronomical Equipment

Despite all recent technological advances, there is still something special about seeing the wonders of the night sky with the naked eye. I often tell prospective stargazers not to worry too much about exactly what it is they can see in the night sky. After all, when you see a great view of the Earth, you probably won't know the name of all the mountains, lakes, and other sights you can see. However, you can still enjoy and marvel at the beautiful views of the natural splendour of our planet. It's the same with astronomy.

For thousands of years, this was the only way to see the night sky. This changed in 1610 when Galileo first turned a telescope skywards. The view through such instruments can be quite impressive. In books, DVDs, and the internet, you can find many stunning images of planets, galaxies and nebula from large observatories and spacecraft. However, there is nothing like seeing for yourself an object in the night sky with your own eyes or through some form of optical aid. I liken this to watching a sporting occasion, concert or theatre production live or on TV. The live view will always be far more exciting and memorable.

I am frequently asked about what equipment someone should get for astronomy. There is a considerable amount of equipment available at varying prices. My advice to anyone is to start small. Then, as the level of interest grows, a choice can be made depending on the level of interest and budget.

Maps and charts

If you are going somewhere new, you will inevitably take a map with you or obtain a local area map on arrival. It's just the same when you are stargazing. You need a decent map or chart of the sky. Many are freely available freely over the internet. Several UK daily newspapers include a guide to the night sky for the forthcoming month. Many books and magazines are available, and you can get "apps" for your mobile phone or tablet. One of my recommendations is to buy a "planisphere". These devices are available in most bookshops for about £10 to £15. They comprise two printed round cards joined together at the centre, with a clear window on the uppermost one. By moving the two together to a specific position, you will obtain a view of the sky for a required date and time. There are three specific ones available for the northern, equatorial and southern skies. Whenever I visit the southern hemisphere, I take one with me. It is handy as a basic guide to what is visible.

Smartphone and tablet "Apps"

In recent years it has been possible to obtain astronomy "apps", and these are very useful. Simply hold your phone or tablet up to the sky, and it will tell you exactly what you are looking at. Some even have a transparent sky where you see the stars and planets in the foreground over whatever background you are looking at. This is very useful in identifying features close to or below your horizon. The only problem with these apps is that you have to ensure that your location is accurately set. Most update your location automatically, but this does rely on you having a good signal available at all times.

This is not always the case when for instance, you are on holiday. I have lost count of how often this becomes a problem on some cruise ships that tend to have limited or poor Wi-Fi access.

Over many years I have often undertaken group stargazing sessions, and whilst describing just what is visible, I have frequently been interrupted by people telling me, for example: "*You are telling us that star is Sirius, but according to my app, it's Rigel*" If I then try to set it up correctly for them, the rest of the group will understandably get restless. So, I have made it a rule not to do so during group sessions. Instead, I ask people to check with me later if they have a query. Another problem I find is when you identify an object on the screen, and you try to show it to your friend or companion. No matter how hard you try, you will inevitably change the direction of the screen. Therefore, what you were looking at will have moved, and you will lose the object you want them to see. Despite these issues, they are an excellent tool for casual stargazing and for individual use.

Using an optical aid for astronomy

Whilst naked eye astronomy is very rewarding and satisfying, eventually, you will want to see more. This is when you need to consider some form of optical aid. There is a vast range of equipment available, ranging in quality, size and price. The basic principle of any form of visual aid is that it collects as much light as possible and magnifies the object you see through the eyepiece. One of the best descriptions I ever heard about a telescope is that it is a "light bucket". The bigger the bucket, the more light you can collect, and the more you can magnify it. You can use a high-powered eyepiece in any device, but unless you have collected a large amount of light in your "bucket," the magnification will be fuzzy and poorly defined.

Binoculars

By far, the most useful piece of equipment I recommend for those starting up in astronomy is a pair of binoculars. Binoculars are fundamentally just two small telescopes side by side. Being so, they can easily be held up to the eyes without you getting tired arms. They can also be relatively inexpensive and be used not just for astronomy but also for bird watching and looking at distant views. Monoculars or spotting telescopes are also available, which are basically just small telescopes.

A good pair of binoculars will show the craters and seas on the Moon, the stellar composition of the Milky Way, the moons of Jupiter and possibly the rings of Saturn. As mentioned previously, we can, with the naked eye, see stars down to about magnitude 6. However, using a good pair of binoculars, you may be able to see down to magnitude 10.

When using a pair, you will notice they usually have a series of numbers on them. Such as 7x35, 7x50 or 10x50. The first number is the power or magnification of the binoculars. For instance, a 10x50 pair will magnify the object you are looking at by 10 times. The second figure is the diameter of the lens at the front of the binoculars in millimetres. This is called the "aperture" or "object-glass". The larger the aperture, the more light you can gather and magnify. The larger the numbers, the more powerful the binoculars. However, there is a downside; the bigger the number, the heavier the binoculars will be. The weight may not be an issue at first but holding a pair up to your eyes for an extended period will prove tiring, and you may find that you cannot keep them steady. It is possible to stabilise the view with a tripod. You can also use a frame or harness to hold them stable. Another helpful device is a mirror placed in front of the binoculars to reflect the image by 90 degrees. This enables you to use a tripod and look down into the binoculars to see up into the night sky. However, you have to make sure the mirror is coated on the front side, not the back, to ensure no double vision issues.

A refracting telescope Note the sturdy tripod.

Telescopes

There are numerous types of telescopes, of which there are two basic types.

A. The Refracting telescope:

This is the type first used by Galileo in 1610. They comprise a set of lenses in a tube, a large object-glass at one end and an eyepiece at the other narrower end. The object-glass enables the light from the object being observed to be brought to a focus where it is magnified by the eyepiece

Small refractors are ideal for beginners and provide excellent images of the Moon and planets, but the relatively small aperture size makes them less suitable for what we term "deep-sky" observing of galaxies and nebulae. Such refractors have an object-glass size of around 50 mm (4 inches). This limits their ability to see fainter objects. Larger ones are available, but they tend to be quite expensive

B. The Reflecting telescope:

This type of telescope was first designed by Isaac Newton and are usually called "Newtonian" reflectors. They use a box or tube, and the aperture or object glass at the bottom is a sizeable concave-shaped mirror. A small mirror is placed toward the top of the tube, which intercepts the light and reflects it to a focus at the eyepiece. The lack of a large lens makes the reflector lighter in weight and less expensive than a similarly sized refractor.

There are many other types of reflecting telescopes, such as Dobsonians, Cassegrain and Schmidt-Cassegrain's. These all have the same basic features of a Newtonian, a large mirror, which brings the collected light to a focus wherever the eyepiece is located. Most smaller and mid-sized reflectors tend to be relatively inexpensive and easily transported and set up. This makes them a good choice for the newcomer.

Most astronomical telescopes provide the observer with an inverted image. Whether it is inverted or the right way up is irrelevant when looking at astronomical objects. To turn an image the right way up requires an additional "correcting" lens. Every time the light passes through a lens, the image will be slightly degraded. To maximise the image quality, a correcting lens is not usually included. Some telescopes do however provide such a lens or prism to correct the image for terrestrial use.

The IOMAS 16-inch telescope (Reflector).

Telescope Mountings

However, while a large aperture size is preferable, one of the most vital components of any telescope is a good, sturdy mount. The slightest movement or vibration will be magnified by the telescope's power when viewing through a telescope. A poor or flimsy tripod or mount will effectively make the telescope useless for deep sky observations. You may well get reasonable views of bright objects such as the Moon or planets, but that is all.

I am frequently asked about telescopes as introductory instruments for new astronomers. My advice is always to carefully check the mount it comes with. If it is a flimsy desktop tripod, my advice will always be to leave well alone. A decent mounting will make all the difference for a little more money.

As with telescopes, there are two basic types. The Altazimuth mount and the Equatorial mount.

A. Altazimuth mounts:

These provide a telescope with free movement up and down (altitude) and left to right (azimuth). Any telescope on a small tripod can be described as being altazimuth mounted.

B. Equatorial mounts:

Utilises a mounting system which enables a telescope to be aligned precisely for your location. In an equatorial mounting, the telescope's axis is aligned parallel to the Earth's axis. The telescope can then be controlled easily using slow-motion controls that minimise excessive contact with the telescope or wobbling. It allows the object in view to remain visible in the eyepiece for longer. Using equatorially mounted telescopes means that a "clock drive" can be used. The telescope is then driven and keeps the observed object in the field of view as the Earth turns on its axis. The IOMAS telescope shown above is mounted equatorially.

Some years ago, I purchased a second hand, equatorially mounted 8-inch Cassegrain reflector. When I took it home, I tried to use it but was quickly frustrated because it would not drive correctly. I eventually learnt that it was used initially in the Bahamas and was set for Nassau at 25 degrees north, not the Manx latitude of 54 degrees north. This was relatively easy to adjust, and it now drives perfectly well.

Most modern telescopes tend now to not use an equatorial mount. Instead, they have computers installed to drive them. Given the technical wizardry of computers, an altazimuth mount is sufficient to control them. These are often called "GoTo" telescopes, and they make finding objects in the sky relatively easy and quick.

A few years ago, at one of the IOMAS star parties, I was using a GoTo telescope and a hand-held controller, which I had used to set it up. You do this by setting the date, time and location into the controller, and you can undertake what is known as "one-star alignment" (two stars are better, but one will generally suffice). First, you place a known star in the centre of the eyepiece. You then confirm this on the controller, and when you have done so, the telescope should then be correctly aligned. I then told the computer to take the telescope to the Andromeda Galaxy (M31). It did so, and I was delighted to find it was there right in the middle of my eyepiece.

As you develop your interest in astronomy, there are many other accessories and pieces of equipment you can purchase, such as a set of eyepieces with different focal lengths or filters which block various wavelengths of light to enhance your viewing. There are also Solar filters available for safe viewing of the Sun.

It is not commonly known, but Solarscope Ltd. Isle of Man, manufactures solar telescopes with special filters that permit direct observing of the Sun. These specialist instruments are sold throughout the world. The object-glass end of these telescopes has the words Isle of Man engraved upon them.

IMPORTANT

Never look directly at the Sun without using an approved solar filter which are placed at the aperture end of a telescope, either over the object-glass of a refractor or at the open end of a reflector tube. Sunlight through a telescope can severely burn your eyes and cause permanent blindness. Avoid telescopes sold with included or separate solar eyepiece filters. These are very dangerous and should never be used. The only appropriate filter that should be utilised fits over the telescope's aperture. My strongest advice is not to use any type of solar filter. There are specialist Solar telescopes available, including some made on the Isle of Man, but leave these to the experts and use the projection technique. This is when you carefully align your telescope on the Sun (using the shadow, not by looking at the Sun). Project an image at the eyepiece end of the telescope onto a screen or piece of card.

Astrophotography

When I was younger, the only way to see those dramatic images of the planets, galaxies and nebulae was in books or films, which used large telescopes in observatories. Today modern photography enables excellent pictures to be taken using just a tripod and a DSLR camera.

You can relatively easily capture star trails and obtain good images of the Moon and planets. I have captured images by holding a mobile phone camera up to a telescope eyepiece on many occasions. There is a tremendous amount of guidance on taking such great photographs in books and online. Such developments have brought a whole new group of people to astronomy.

However, you might just want to see these sights for yourself with your naked eye and be fascinated by the wonders of the world of astronomy. I can recommend wrapping up warm, going outside on a clear night with the family or a group of friends. Use some sun loungers or a blanket. When you look up at a clear night sky the view can be breath-taking. It has to be one of the best sights in the natural world you can see, and it fills you with a sense of awe and wonder. I have had the subject described to me as "mental yoga" and I can understand why. You can lose yourself in the stars.

Acknowledgements

I am very grateful to many people who have generously given their time and expertise in the compilation of this book. Thank you to you all for inspiring and encouraging my literary efforts.

A special mention must go to my beta readers Chis and Nicole Stott, Graham Gordon, Jeff Dugdale and John Cuddy, and to my proofreader Tony Pass for their dedication and persistence in what was an onerous task. I am extremely grateful to all of you.

I am delighted that so many photographers kindly permitted me to use their spectacular images throughout the book. A big thank you to Ron Strathdee, Dave Storey, James Martin, Kevin Deakes, Carl Hough, Glen Whorrall, Sue Jones, Pete Geddes, James Brew, Jake Huxley, Bill Bevan, John Taylor, Rob Farrington and Tracy Roberts. I hope that such wonderful images will inspire readers.

Through many years, and during the compilation of this book, I have been helped and encouraged by many people to whom I am very grateful. These include John "Dog" Callister, Gary Corlett, Celia Marshall, Judith Ley, Tim Craine, Sue King, Ralfy Mitchell, Lionel Skillicorn, Kelvin Woolmer, Jean Fullerton, Alison Nevin, and many of my friends and colleagues, in the Isle of Man Astronomical Society, the University College of Mann, especially Paul Wilkinson, Cathy Lord, Clare Monaghan and Kerry Birchall and the Manx Retirement Association.

Also, several organisations encouraged and assisted me in a variety of ways, in particular, Manx National Heritage, The IOM Post Office, Manx Radio, Viking Ocean Cruises, Carnival Cruises, Peel Talent, The Astro Space Stamp Society, Miles Cowsill and all at Lily Publications. This publication has been supported by Culture Vannin, and a special thank you must go to their director Bresha Maddrell, and also to Visit Isle of Man, in particular Jade Foster for your encouragement and valuable support.

Finally, to my wife Sandra, whose tireless support and encouragement led me to see this project through to completion. I am eternally grateful.

A glossary of astronomical terms in Manx Gaelic

English	Manx
Andromeda	Yn Ven Ghjeulit
Aquarius	Yn Ymmyrkagh Ushtey
Aries	Y Rea
Astronaut	Troailtagh spoar
Auiriga	Yun Fainagh
Binary Star	Rollage Ghooble
Bootes	Y Bochilley
Cancer	Y Partan
Capricorn	Y Goayr
Comet	Comaid
Constellation	Rollageagh
Dark skies	Speyryn dorraghey
Dark sky	Speyr ghorraghey
Earth	Y Cruinney / Y Seihll
Eclipse	Bodjal
Full moon	lane eayst
Gemini	Ny Lannoonyn
Green Flash	Soilshey-bio
International Year of Astronomy	Blein Eddyr Ashoonagh Rollageydys
Keep your eyes on the sky, but your feet on the ground	Freill dty hooillyn er y speyr, agh dty chassyn er y thalloo
Leo (Sickle)	Y Lion / Y Corran
Libra	Ny Meihaghyn
Mars	Mart
Mercury	Mercur
Milky Way, the great way of King Orry	Raad Mooar Ree Gorree
Moon	Eayst
Northern light	Lossan y Twoaie
Orion	Y Shelgeyr Mooar
Perseus	Yn Whing
Pisces	Ny Eeastyn
Pleiades	Y Trilleen
Pole Star	Rollage Hwoaie
Sagittarius	Y Sideyr
Saturn	Sarn
Scorpio	Y Scorpion
Sky	Speyr
Stargazer	Rollageyder
Sun	Grian

Sunspot	Cron greiney
Taurus	Y Tarroo
The Plough	Arc y Twoaie / Yn Arc Mooar / Y Keeaght
Universe	Tuinney
Ursa Major	Y Mucawin Mooar
Ursa Minor	Y Mucawin Beg / Y Keeaght Beg
Venus	Baytnag / Badlag
Vernal Equinox	Cormid traa-arree
Virgo	Y Voidyn

Index